Ha[...]

with love
Rowan, Ker + Holly
x.x.

THE DARLING BUDS OF MAY
BOOK OF THE SEASONS

THE DARLING BUDS OF MAY
BOOK OF THE SEASONS

H.E. BATES

Edited by Neil Philip
Illustrated by Llewellyn Thomas

MICHAEL JOSEPH

LONDON

First published by
Michael Joseph Limited, 27 Wrights Lane, London W8
1992

ISBN 0 7181 3612 8

A CIP catalogue record for this book is available from the
British Library.

Edited, designed and produced by
The Albion Press Limited, P.O. Box 52, Princes Risborough,
Aylesbury, Buckinghamshire

Designer: Emma Bradford
Project manager: Elizabeth Wilkes

Typesetting and colour origination by York House, London
Printed and bound in Great Britain by Eagle Colourbooks Limited, Glasgow

CONTENTS

SPRING

SPRING CAME too early, false with bursts of blue warmth in March, a bright glinting on brooks and river and a few first spare primroses in copses southward of the town after late falls of snow.

THE FEAST OF JULY

THE BOY and the old man were ploughing the field that lay on the valley-slope. The plough was drawn by a single horse, an old bony chestnut. It was early March, but already the weather was beautiful, and it was like an April day. Great clouds of white and grey and stormy blue kept sailing in endless flocks across the bright sky from the west, into the face of the morning sun. The cloud-shadows, travelling at a great pace down the sloping field, vanished and then reappeared on the other side of the valley, racing across the brown and green of the planted and unplanted fields. There was a feeling everywhere of new light, which created in turn a feeling of new life. The light was visible even in the turned land, which lay divided into regular stripes of shadow and light at every furrow. The earth, a dark clay, turned up in long sections which shone in the sun like steel, only a little duller in tone than the ploughshare itself.

THE PLOUGH

As THEY drove along the high road from the station the sun sank behind the dark line of woods in the west and the cold, still March twilight began to drop over the fields. The young wheat was showing in feathery lines of the brightest green and the sallows were half-gold, half-silver among the young hazel trees, dusty-yellow with catkins, in the roadside copses. The earth was dried to a sand colour by wind and sunshine; the evening sky was clear, wind-blown, without a cloud.

THE FALLOW LAND

SHE WOKE at midday next day to an unexpected, astonishing sight: a deep late March snow. Thickly, a foot or more, it lay smooth on everything, a pure level crust, as much blue as white in the strong March sun, transforming garden, bushes, fossiled willows and the fields between the normally grey and desolate dykes with an amazingly tranquil and uplifting beauty.

With cold disbelief she stood and stared at it from the bedroom window. Already the hot March sun had begun to melt it on the southward side of the house. The roof was dripping like a running spring.

THE SIMPLE LIFE

THE COLD left us very reluctantly. A long succession of white savage weeks brought us to a March in which there was no sign of spring. The banks of the lake were still wrapped in white marble waves. Bitter winds rattled the dry reeds and always when the swans took to flight you heard the strange whine of their passage, like the wind's echo.

All at once summer began in April. Orchards suddenly offered a rich and shining feast of plum bloom. In sheets of almost unbearably brilliant emerald young wheat rose from under the snow and soon primroses, together with crowds of white anemones, spread themselves everywhere about the copses, the lakeside and the banks of the little river where Harry had already started to cast for trout. It was really warm at last and there was a great chorus of bird-song everywhere.

A MOMENT IN TIME

THE SUN went down across the valley. Beyond the stone swords of nine church spires it set fire to a sky that for a long time smouldered with bronze and orange and a far high glow of pale pure spring green. Under twilight the smell of spring earth warmed by sun seemed to thicken all along the copse-edge. As she looked up she could have sworn that the fiery tips of the larches had lengthened since late afternoon. Even after the sun had gone down and the branches were black again in the clear blue spring twilight she could hear the one exposed voice of a thrush whistling madly against darkness and the thin pure echo of a solitary lark in the field below.

THE FEAST OF JULY

'Mrs Bartholomew!'

She went outside. The strong clear March sun was already hot. Snow was melting and dripping everywhere. The power and brilliance of the sun had also a curious effect of magnification. Framed against snow and the clearest of clear blue skies the boy seemed to be altogether taller, bigger in frame, than when sitting at the breakfast table. Snow-light also heightened remarkably the remorseless young brilliance of the eyes.

He raised a hand to the sky. 'Up there. Straight overhead. See him?'

She lifted her face, eyes dazzled.

'Can't see a thing.'

'Straight up. You can hear him anyway, can't you?'

She stood for some moments staring and listening, eyes dazzled by sun, neither seeing nor hearing a thing. Then she finally managed to tune her ears to the thin trembling of lark song, cascading down, as it were, from a great vacuum.

'Oh! I hear it now. Marvellous. But I still can't see a thing.'

He dropped his snow shovel on the path, walked down the path to join her and pointed to the sky.

'You're not looking in the right direction.' He stood close by her, holding her right arm just below the elbow. 'No, not that way. Overhead. More overhead.'

She stared into the sky with eyes screwed up, again seeing nothing.

'I said your eyes were keener than mine.'

'It's farther up than you're looking, Mrs Bartholomew. Look farther up.'

She laughed. 'I'm looking a million miles up now.'

'Perhaps you're looking too much against the sun.'

'I'm just plain stupid, that's what.'

Suddenly she gave a cry. In a moment of unexpected revelation both sound and sight of the lark, from a height that seemed to her impossibly distant, merged together. She became conscious of a moment of great, simple, exquisite pleasure and in the unremitting thrill of it she actually threw up both hands.

'It's the most beautiful thing in the world,' she said, 'it's the most beautiful sound I ever heard.'

THE SIMPLE LIFE

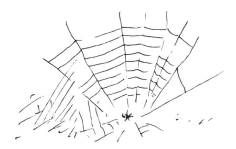

WHEN SHE came up the hill on the following afternoon it was with the thought of Parker, rather than the hat, uppermost in her mind. She did not conceive the hat as an important thing. Spring was coming across the valley and puffs of blossom, like tranquil smoke, rose everywhere about the pastures below the hill. Under a sharp blue sky the beeches were brilliant masses of almost transparent lace-like leaf and it puzzled her, almost irked her, that a man could live as Parker lived in the spring time: womanless, unswept, curtains unwashed, the old crust of winter still clinging everywhere like a frowsy mould.

DULCIMA

16

It is one of those early April mornings that are neither warm nor cold and the light on the land is a kind of spring half-light, not shadow and not sun, a soft and rather treacherous glimmering from behind the north-west cloud. The wind is quite strong and in open places finger-cold, and there is a continuous dancing everywhere of branch and flower and even grass. On the open green outside the house there is only a row of elms and chestnuts to break the wind, and the trees are still not in leaf. So the wind comes straight across, rippling the pond into a little sea, with dark fitful little waves that must be quite stormy for the moorhens. The grass on the green is a thin speary grass, grown tussocky, and the rains of winter have flattened it into a kind of brownish-yellow mattress. It hardly moves in the wind. Above it, however, many lady-smocks, standing in small mauve companies, dance and fret incessantly. There are no other flowers, except an odd dandelion. or two and some patches of celandine almost hidden by grass, and except for them and the yellow fluttering of distant daffodils through garden fences, it might still be winter.

THROUGH THE WOODS

The wood was flooded with April sunlight, but shallow pools of rain lay wherever there were hollows in the black earth under the oak trees. Black rings of ashes were dotted about the ground where tramps had made their fires and rested, and primroses were blooming everywhere at the feet of young hazel trees. The wind that blew the hazels with a soft sound one against another was sweet and warm and laden with the scent of the primroses. It was like the breath of a new life.

ON THE ROAD

By April things had begun to move. The rows of herbs began to look vigorous and full of promise. Turned over and hoed, the earth was sweet and black. The two girls planted fresh supplies of plants, new varieties, and sowed seeds. They got up early and worked on into the bright spring evenings, and in the evenings, after a warm day, they could smell the forest, the strong, vigorous and yet almost drowsy odour of a great mass of trees breaking into leaf. They were enchanted by the new life, by an existence in which, as never before, they felt they had a purpose. They lived physically. Tired out, earth-stained, they came indoors as darkness came on and sat down in the little kitchen-sitting-room in the cottage and sat on without speaking and watched the fading out of the primrosy twilights, their minds dumbly content. Too tired to talk, they ate supper, went to bed early and were up again at six.

BREEZE ANSTEY

HE CAME out of his shop soon after six one April evening and went into Charlotte's Row carrying a bundle of boots on his shoulder. Easter was very near and the sky was a pale, cold green, as if with coming frost. Charlotte's Row was composed of two rows of dark yellowish brick houses which sloped gently downwards towards a railway-arch spanning the lower end; the houses were small, dark and poverty-stricken, with regular holes of entry to backyards, like a line of kennels.

CHARLOTTE'S ROW

ON EASTER Sunday morning nine white pigeons were circling swiftly in the blue air over the backyards of Charlotte's Row, their wings making a sighing sound which rose and fell to a whisper as they surged overhead and wheeled away.

CHARLOTTE'S ROW

HE TOOK to riding the mare about the fields and along the grass of the road-sides. He rode well; it was easy for him to ride with a useless arm. He sometimes branched off and rode along the old green lanes, the forgotten roads of Roman days. Under the high hedges the spring sun was already warm, the dog's mercury shooting green under the budded whitethorn, the sallow buds shining white and fat, like cocoons of silvered silk.

Riding along a green lane one afternoon he passed a girl stooping in the hedge-side, searching for violets. He rode slowly past and looked down at her and she looked up at him, with a violet in her mouth. He waved his hand. She looked at him, startled, and bent her head again. He did not notice whether she was dark or fair; he looked at the white fringe of her petticoat showing under her skirt and the curve of her breast against her costume. When he rode back again she was still there and he reined the mare and spoke to her.

'Good afternoon. Nice lot o' violets I noticed along there by the spinney.'

'Oh! did you?'

'Primroses coming out, too.'

She looked at his arm, lying in its black silk sling under his coat.

'What have *you* been doing to yourself?' she said.

'Breaking my neck.'

They laughed, easier at once with one another. She was a big, fair smooth-limbed girl, she spoke in a semi-refined voice, with a rich tone, a trifle low and half-languid. She carried herself magnificently and her clothes were part of herself, the skirt tight and smooth on her hips and her blouse strained taut on its pearl-buttons by her strong breasts. The violets looked curiously frail and very dark against her big fair hands, covered with beautiful reddish-golden hairs. Her beauty was like the beauty of a great ripe sunflower, burdened with its own luxuriance, her face seemed to be perpetually smiling. Her eyes, large and coloured like the violets she was holding, were full of restless, magnetic life.

They played up to each other, she at moments picking violets as though he were not there and he looking across the land as though he had forgotten her.

'I don't know which are the prettiest,' he said, 'the violets or the one who's getting 'em.'

'You've got a fine horse,' she said wickedly.

'I'll give her to you!' he boasted.

'You will?'

'I said I would!'

It was a great excuse to get off the horse and stand nearer to her.

'There you are,' he said. 'There's your horse. Can you ride?'

'No.'

'Would you like to ride? Come on, I'll teach you.'

She flushed and hesitated.

'Here, put your foot in the stirrup and catch hold of me. Whoa! She don't know you yet. Put your foot in the stirrup. Now!'

It was all over in a moment and she was sitting in the saddle. She sat splendidly, and her limbs, smooth and heavy, seemed at once part of the horse. His hand brushed her leg as she swung up and her skirt was flung back, showing her stocking. She made a great show of smoothing the skirt into place, but she sat astraddle and her long skirts were heavy and awkward and he watched her with a grin on his face as she went from one difficulty to another.

'How do you feel?' he said finally.

'I don't know what you'd think if I told you,' she said.

He smiled inscrutably. 'Ready?'

She nodded and he patted the mare softly and she moved off. The girl jerked in the saddle and uttered a heavy, luxuriant kind of laugh and tugged the reins.

'Sit easy. Don't pull her. Just sit easy and let her take you.' He rested his hand boldly on her heavy thigh. 'I've got you.'

She looked down upon him with ironic amusement.

'So it seems.'

'You wouldn't like to fall, would you?' he said.

'Not yet!'

Every word of their bantering speech was full of significance; they took pains to make their meanings dark, but when their meanings were darkest they managed in some way, by some look or smile or gesture, to make them plain.

They progressed along the lane to where, by a wood, the grass was uncut by cart-tracks. The girl reined in the horse.

'I want to gallop,' she said.

'You'll come off,' he warned her.

'A nice chance for you!' she flashed.

'All right, gallop,' he said. He clicked on the mare. 'Let yourself go with the horse and keep your knees tight.'

The mare moved off and quickened into a trot and the girl rode far up the lane and turned at last and began to return. She could not break the horse into a canter and she abandoned her body to the motions of trotting. Her limbs moved tremulously and her breasts trembled under her blouse and when she finally reached him again she was hot and excited, her eyes brimming with an extraordinary look of pleasure.

He handed her down. He could feel the warmth of her body even before touching her.

'Like it?' he said.

'Wonderful.'

'You'll be stiff,' he told her as he took the bridle again.

She was panting softly. Her brilliant fair hair had shaken itself down a little, her bosom was rising and dropping with great breaths. Her body gave off the faint warm odour of excitement.

'I've lost my violets!' she exclaimed suddenly.

'I'll go back.'

'No, I'll come again tomorrow.'

'You'll come again tomorrow,' he repeated significantly.

'If it's fine.'

She was picking violets on the outskirts of the spinney on the following afternoon when he rode up. He smiled down at her from his horse.

'Well, well,' he said.

'Well, well.'

He dismounted, the mare began grazing, and he walked to where the girl was stooping in the sunshine.

'Like violets?' he said.

'It's their scent and their colour,' she said. 'So dark. I like dark things,' she flashed.

'Ah? Don't like primroses?'

'Not so much.'

He looked at her fair hair, almost a pale primrose colour itself.

'I do,' he said.

They looked steadily at each other for a second or two. Their eyes put life and significance into their words. They smiled with a kind of ironic innocence.

'Well, well,' he said.

'Well, well,' she whispered slowly.

It was a fine game. They were like flint and steel to each other; the sparks flew easily, never breaking into real fire. It was exhilarating. He had never played this kind of game with Deborah and he was pleased to

22

find that he could play it so well.

'How's your arm?' she said.

'Getting better, worse luck.'

She smiled.

'Like to gallop again?' he said. 'Come on,' he urged.

'In a moment. This time you must hold my violets.'

They went through all the elaborate play of getting her into the saddle again. She smoothed her skirts and sat like a queen and he thought she looked even more striking than on the previous day.

'Tchk! Tchk!'

She rode away up the lane and turned and came back again; she trotted the horse both ways, and when she brought the horse to a standstill again her face was hot and excited and her hair was falling over her face.

He caught her by the waist as she slid off the horse and she leaned heavily upon him.

They walked up into the wood. He kept his hand about her waist. He asked her name. When she told him he did not catch it and she rolled it out again in her rich voice, lingering over its syllables: 'Alma Wolstenholm.' The wood was coming to life; the sunshine filtered down warmly through the spring boughs, lighting up the emerald dog's mercury and the earliest primroses. The scent of earth rose up strong but elusive. She took great breaths of it, filling her lungs until the buttons of her blouse were strained. When the topmost button slipped from its loop he saw the pink woollen string threaded through her bodice; that too was strained over her tight full flesh. She did not button up her blouse and he slipped his hand over her shoulder and touched her neck. She started. He could feel her heart throbbing. She looked superb. 'Ah! Give us a kiss,' he said. She turned and thrust her mouth up to him and kissed him. It was like the tired dry earth sucking up rain; she drank at his mouth, greedily and with ecstasy, as though he were a fountain of blissful strength and delight that she could not leave until the very depths of her soul were satisfied.

THE FALLOW LAND

BUT IF I have sometimes been glad to leave a wood by day I have oftener been sorry. I sat once in a wood on the north border of Bedfordshire, in April, by a keeper's hut, eating an orange. It was perfect weather, quiet and sunny, with a little windy blowing about of the hazels. I had walked up the wood, along still ridings, seeing more primroses and also more oxlips, which are like wild polyanthus, than I had ever seen before or in fact than I have ever seen since. By the keeper's hut there was a biggish pool. Very still, overshadowed by trees, it looked like a stretch of black glass. All over the place was a windy clapping and brushing of bare ash and hazel and, every time the wind turned, a great breath of primrose scent.

Suddenly there was an unexpected stirring about the pool: a flicker of brown, almost fawn, and then another and another. The first I took for a rabbit. Even about the second I had some doubt. After the third and fourth and fifth I had no doubt: they were young fox-cubs. They came tumbling up out of the holes in the pond-bank, in and out, up and down, rolling over and over, playing an endless game of chivvy with

each other, until I could count thirteen. As a boy, I once held a lion-cub in my hands: he was a fawny gold and like plush, a wonderfully soft golden cat with a sleepy blinking face. Those fox-cubs playing in the woods were very like him: so many little fawny-gold cats playing with a kind of pretty devilry up and down the banks of the pool, running out into the primroses, doubling back, rolling each other over, their light fur all the time ruffled and rosetted by the light wind, until they seemed like the prettiest creatures in the world. I sat there for a long time, watching them. The wind was just right, blowing from them to me, and they never suspected my presence. They were endlessly fascinating, tireless in their own devilries, lovely with their sun-coloured fawn and their grace of movement up and down that steep bank, on the edge of the water. And finally I had only myself to blame for upsetting it all. Not satisfied, I moved nearer, slowly and, as I thought, quite soundlessly. Getting much nearer, I stood still. I could see them better. They had still no suspicion of me. Then, in a moment, I moved on again. I made no sound, but in a second they were all arrested, electrically, in alarm. They stopped for a single second, cocked their heads and gave one look at me. In another moment they had gone tumbling down like golden balls into the dark fox-holes, out of sight. And I have never, by some damnable chance, seen a fox-cub since.

THROUGH THE WOODS

ON A day in late April, she took the baby and carried him down through the yard, in the sunshine, to where the fields began. Hedgerows were breaking everywhere into bright new leaf. Primroses lay in thick pale drifts under the shelter of them and under clumps of ash and hornbeam. In every turn of wind there was a whitening of anemones, with cowslips trembling gold about the pasture.

She lifted the baby up, in the sunshine, against the blue spring sky, and laughed and shook him gently, showing him the world of leaf and flower and corn.

'Look at all the flowers!' she said. 'Look at the corn! The corn looks good, doesn't it? It's going to be good this year, isn't it? Look at it all! – isn't the corn beautiful?'

High above her, on the hill, there was a sound of endless lark song and in the fields the young curved lines of corn were wonderfully fresh and trembling in the sun.

THE GOOD CORN

TOWARDS FOUR o'clock she came upon a wood of young oak trees; she sat down there and felt that the day would remain imprinted on her mind for ever. She had never before seen the windflowers sweeping up from a hollow dark with wintry ivy leaves, modest, trembling, delicate things, white as if kissed by snow, dancing and quivering in the faint wind under the bare trees. Primroses in thousands, in clusters of pale yellow, were blooming shy and still among the stiff dark spears of

unbudded hyacinth leaves. The wood was full of a trembling virgin light and the air was fragrant with the odour of the flowers and the promise of earth. The long, slender wands of a young ash-tree kept clapping together overhead with a restless sound. There was a pathway in the wood and presently she walked on, not touching the flowers, only gazing on them in a dreamy, bewildered way. But suddenly the possessive instinct of womanhood, the primitive need for beauty, made her fall to her knees and begin filling her hands. She gathered windflowers and primroses, bunching them separately, and then in a wide clear hollow of earth she found violets, heavily fragrant, dark and white. The purple flowers were solemn and mystic, and the white shone with a virgin purity, hanging discreet and lovely on their stems as the heads of nuns.

CHARLOTTE'S ROW

IT WAS not until the end of April, when the weather was warmer and he had begun to get back his strength, that he troubled to think about the spring. He saw it emotionlessly even then. He became fully aware of it only when the damson trees came into blossom at last, in the green orchard. He first saw the trees, consciously, one Sunday morning, as he went back home after helping with the cows. The black trees had changed by a miracle to white. They stood transfigured, the blossom a miracle of whiteness. The half-transparent petals were so light that there was hardly a shadow on the grass. The cowslips had come out too, rich yellow in the white-petalled orchard, and he could see the bees

27

working in them and in the damson trees. Separately, and then together, he could smell the scents of cowslips and grass and damson blossom. It was quiet except for the sound the bees made. And he stood listening to them and watching them and looking at the white blossom and breathing the scent of it all until he could stand no longer.

THE POACHER

SPRING CAME to Evensford about the end of April with shabby flower-ings of brown wallflowers on allotment grounds, with dusty daffodils behind the iron railings of street front gardens. Earth everywhere had been pulverized by black frost to a saltiness that blew grittily about on dry spring winds, cornering fish-and-chip papers in Evensford's many alley-ways. In the town there was hardly anything to distinguish what was now the spring from what had been the winter except that the days were longer and not so cold and that the view across the valley showed ice no longer. There were now only broken lakes of receding water to which swans returned for a last few days in great white flocks, before they too broke up and paired for summer nesting.

Behind the walls of the Aspen ground, all across the park, spring came so differently that it was another world. Rooks did not begin nesting in the old chestnut trees behind the lime avenue and in the big elms above the gate-house until the middle of April, cawing all day in slow-greening branches. Everything was late that year. The brook thawed and all along its wet banks white anemones came fluttering into bloom, together with big soft white violets, pure as snowdrops, and primroses among blobby islands of king-cup under yellow hazel boughs. Whenever I went through the gates and along the avenue there was a wonderful belling chorus of thrushes that expanded under a closing framework of branches, madly and most wonderfully in the long pale twilight when the air was green with young leaves and the acid of new grass after sunset and spring rain. Nearer the house there were random drifts of pale blue anemone, bright as clippings of sky among black clusters of butchers broom, and then, under limes and in grass along every slope leading up to the house, daffodils in thousands, in crowds of shaking yellow flame. Some earlier, far-sighted Aspen had planted great groups of blue cedar about the place and they rose in high conical groups, greyish after winter, to be touched, as spring came, with young delicate sprouts of blue-green fire. Acres of grass flowed away under plantings of horse chestnut that flared, by the end of April, into thick blossom that soon became scattered by wind into rose-white drifts on paths and terraces and even as far as the elm avenue that led to more spinneys of primrose and hazel and white violet on the western side.

By May the spinneys were thick with bluebells.

LOVE FOR LYDIA

SPRING CAME slowly and reluctantly to the marsh. By the very end of April certain stretches of the long grey dykes were at last gold with kingcups, with light feathery sweeps of lady-smock mauve between. An impassioned ceaseless song of skylarks filled the air. There came a day when she saw, for the first time, the blue and copper arrow of a kingfisher.

THE SIMPLE LIFE

29

APART FROM the main holding with its little farmyard my grandfather rented from time to time two other fields, both pasture and both of about five acres in area, one for the purpose of gathering a stack of hay, the other for grazing one of the unfortunate ponies; but it was really about the little farmyard, with its clucking hens and squealing pigs, that the horizon of my world extended. The crest of the valley here is quite high, wide and open to every searing, soaking wind. On a really clear fine day it was possible here to pick out no less than nine of the church spires for which Northamptonshire is justly famous. Few trees and no great woodlands were there to break the view. Ash, hawthorn and elm, with here and there a few small oaks, made up the general pattern of trees; the beeches, sweet chestnuts, turkey oats and white-beams which I now know and love in the south country were never to be seen.

Nevertheless, sparsely clothed as it was, the land in spring and summer was a great thrilling palpitation of bird song. I can see now huge droves of grey elephantine April cloud-shadows rushing across the valley before the western wind and feel the cut of ice in the air each time the sun went in. Along the headlands flowered yellow drifts of coltsfoot, doubly precious because this was a countryside with no primroses, no bluebells, no kingcups, none of Shakespeare's beloved lady-smocks, still to me one of the high aristocrats of England's spring flowers. Above it all a pee-witting chorus of plovers would beat strongly at the air, but never strongly enough to drown the celestial choirs of skylarks, for whose nests I was constantly going in diligent search along the plough furrows. Kestrels hovered above, too, poised for the long darting kill, and the May hedgerows clinked with the pink-pink of chaffinches, not long since one of England's commonest birds but now, alas, almost a rarity. And then in summer the yellowhammers, the endless drowsy repetition of 'a little bit of bread and no cheese', and the occasional whistle of swan wings beating up from the river.

THE VANISHED WORLD

30

MORTIMER WALKED across the farmyard and opening the paddock gate went down the cart-track under the willow trees. It was the first Sunday in May, the sun warming the earth steadily, fetching up its rich scents. Mortimer caught the odour of dandelions, the wine-like sweetness of cowslips, the scent of the many grasses. He walked slowly, stopping at intervals to pick a cowslip-head growing in the wet bank by the trickle of water. Among the cowslips little cuckoo-pints waved light clusters of mauve feathers, and gathering a stalk of flowers he put it in his buttonhole, smelling its light fragrance first. The air was still and windless, the songs of skylarks and the odd drowsy notes of cuckoos breaking it gently, the flutter of the thin young willow leaves falling upon it with a light murmur, like the echo of a dim breath.

At the corner of the field was a stile. He climbed it slowly. He hooked his basket on a hawthorn stump, sat on the stile for a moment or two and looked over the field beyond.

The field was a sea of cowslips. Taking long breaths, he stared until his eyes began to water and the cowslips seemed to swim together, surging up and down the field in tawny-golden waves. Finally he climbed slowly down and walked across the slope of the field, into the full tide of the cowslips, like a man wading into a yellow lake.

THE FALLOW LAND

31

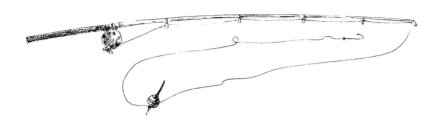

GOING OFF with his grandmother across the town one evening in May he returned with a fishing-rod and some hooks and a little red float that the old woman had given him. 'You may as well take it and be a fisherman like the others have been,' she said. 'All your family were fishermen, every one of them. I used to weep my eyes sore wondering where Eli had gone, going away in the morning and not showing his face till dark again. When he could fish that man would never work, and when he was working he was never happy till he was fishing again. You spring from a lazy lot, my boy. A lazy, dreamy, good-for-nothing, soft-hearted lot, that's what you spring from.'

CHARLOTTE'S ROW

32

ONE WARM fine spring evening we wandered along the wooded banks of a brook, probably a small tributary of the River Welland. Primroses, kingcups, white and purple violets and Shakespeare's lady-smocks bloomed everywhere about the marshy earth. After some time I stopped to climb a stile and then, suddenly turning my head to look for Con, found myself caught up in an unexpected, swift and passionate embrace, and then kissed long, fully and ardently on the lips.

How I recovered from this totally unexpected but delicious ravaging of my boyhood innocence I find it hard to say; it sometimes seems to me not at all impossible that I might have been left speechless for the rest of my life. There was certainly, at that ecstatic moment, nothing to say; nor could I have said it if I had wanted to; instead I could only offer my lips in further sacrifice, surrendering to an ardour returned by lips ecstatic, compulsive and not wholly inexperienced. It was no longer a question of sweet, devoted friendship; the moment was more like the fusion of two white-hot wires.

THE VANISHED WORLD

THE EVENING was very warm and soft and a deep fragrance of bluebells came from hazel copses above the house as she turned the kitchen furniture into the farmyard and then took the curtains from the windows and hung them, like disintegrating cobwebs, on the clothes line. She scrubbed the kitchen floor, the stove, and the stone steps outside. Water ran like mud, bearing away with it the stale rank odours of old grease, old cooking, old dust, and the curious close stench of winter decay. She washed up the crockery of the past week and opened the windows and let in the spring evening air.

When she had finished all this she walked into the yard to look for Parker. When she could not see him she walked across to a small orchard beyond the cow-barn. Down the hill Parker was harrowing ground for spring seed. The soil was dry and dusty and the tractor seemed to draw behind it a brown and smoky cloud.

Everywhere primroses, with drifts of white anemone, were growing in lush masses under hazel-trees and she gathered a handful while she waited for Parker to come in with the harrow. But after a time there seemed to be something wrong with the tractor and she gave up waiting and went back into the house.

She put the primroses into a little red glass jug on the supper table. She had already laid out all the food she could find, a little bread, a piece of home-killed bacon, and a lump of cheese. Now she sat down to wait for Parker and after about ten minutes he came in.

For some moments he stood on the kitchen threshold with small rabbity eyes transfixed by all he saw. This transfixed narrow stare was not surprised or unbelieving or even doubtful. It was held in suspicion: as if he could not accept it without also accepting that behind it there lay some sort of motive. Nobody did such things for nothing; nobody gave things away without wanting something back.

'I didn't have much time, Mr Parker,' she said, 'but it's a bit better. It's a bit sweeter anyway.'

'Ah,' he said.

DULCIMA

UP ON the higher land, above the village, the morning was magnificent. Cowslips had come out in thousands on the grassland, richer and deeper in colour than the May sunlight. In the hollow below, the land, never enclosed, was like a single hedgeless field, vast and rolling. It was guarded on all sides by a circle of woods. Under the woods the slopes were green with grass, but down in the hollow and beyond the village the light emerald of wheatfields was as vivid and sweet as the cowslip-coloured grass in the clear sunshine.

THE POACHER

35

THE BLACKTHORN tree stooped over the high bank above the road. Its branches were clouded with white blossom and the spring sunlight threw lace-like patterns on the earth that had been trodden bare underneath the tree. The grass of the bank was scattered with big, pale-blue violets and stars of coltsfoot and daisies very like chance black-thorn blossoms that the wind had shaken down. In the hedge behind the blackthorn were companies of pale green lords-and-ladies that had thrust up their unfurled hoods through a thicket of dog's-mercury. They looked cold and stately. The sunlight was sharp and brilliant and against the blue of the sky the blackthorn tree was whiter than a summer cloud.

A FLOWER PIECE

36

IT WAS nearly May before she and Frankie Johnson began to meet again at Pollards' Mill. There were still late violets in the copses but half the oaks were bare. The land seemed to quiver on the edge of winter, holding back, half green, half dark, and sometimes with stubborn banners of snow by woodsides. The young blades of corn would not lift themselves up and larks sang chilly breathless songs, ruffled and buffeted across skies of driving hail-cloud.

Then suddenly, at the end of May, all summer seemed to rush forward in a single sultry breath. With luxuriance the oaks flowered into thick curtains of dusty yellow. In a few days a darkening of leaf knotted copses into solid masses, unlightened except for tips of wild-cherry smoking white in the sun.

The days were so beautiful, thick with sappiness, choked to over-richness with blackbird song, breathless with too-sudden heat that woke the first crowds of May-fly across the glassy water of the millpond, that she could walk for the first time in a summer dress. It was a yellow dress, silk, with sprigs of green fern-frond repeated about it, and the day she first wore it she could feel the softness of May blowing about her skirt again, flowing excitedly across her limbs.

That day, lying on the edge of the millpond, hatless in hot sun, she picked a dandelion stalk, held it against the sky, blew on the ball of seed and felt that she was blowing the final cloud of winter away.

'Five o'clock.' She blew hard at a last fragment of seed. 'Half-past.' Once or twice more she blew on the clinging tuft of seed. 'No: that one doesn't want to go.' She held the bare stalk against the blue May sky before throwing it away. 'Call it half-past five.'

THE SLEEPLESS MOON

37

ONE EARLY summer evening Madge and I were driving through a Kentish village twenty-five miles east of us, in apple orchard country, when she suddenly had reason to stop and make a few purchases at the village shop. As I sat waiting for her in the car I noticed, outside the shop, a ramshackle lorry that had been recently painted a violent electric blue. Two or three minutes later there came out of the shop, in high spirits, a remarkable family: father a perky, sprightly character with dark side-burnings, Ma a youngish handsome woman of enormous girth, wearing a bright salmon jumper and shaking with laughter like a jelly, and six children, the eldest of them a beautiful dark-haired girl of twenty or so. All were sucking at colossal multi-coloured ice-creams and at the same time crunching potato crisps. As they piled into the lorry there was an air of gay and uninhibited abandon about it all. Wild laughter rang through the village street and the whole scene might have come out of Merrie England.

THE WORLD IN RIPENESS

AFTER DISTRIBUTING the eight ice-creams – they were the largest vanilla, chocolate, and raspberry super-bumpers, each in yellow, brown, and almost purple stripes – Pop Larkin climbed up into the cab of the gentian blue, home-painted thirty-hundredweight truck, laughing happily.

'Perfick wevver! You kids all right at the back there? Ma, hitch up a bit!'

Ma, in her salmon jumper, was almost two yards wide.

'I said you kids all right there?'

'How do you think they can hear,' Ma said, 'with you revving up all the time?'

Pop laughed again and let the engine idle. The strong May sunlight, the first hot sun of the year, made the bonnet of the truck gleam like brilliant blue enamel. All down the road, winding through the valley, miles of pink apple orchards were in late bloom, showing petals like light confetti.

'Zinnia and Petunia, Primrose, Victoria, Montgomery, Mariette!' – Pop unrolled the handsome ribbon of six names but heard only five separate answers, each voice choked and clotted with ice-cream.

'Where's Mariette? Ain't Mariette there?'

'I'm here, Pop.'

'That's all right then. Thought you'd fell overboard.'

'No, I'm here, Pop, I'm here.'

'Perfick!' Pop said. 'You think I ought to get more ice-creams? It's so hot Ma's is nearly melted.'

Ma shook all over, laughing like a jelly. Little rivers of yellow, brown, and pinkish-purple cream were running down over her huge lardy hands. In her handsome big black eyes the cloudless blue May sky was reflected, making them dance as she threw out the splendid bank of her bosom, quivering under its salmon jumper. At thirty-five she still had a head of hair like black silk cotton, curly and thick as it fell to her fat olive shoulders. Her stomach and thighs bulged like a hopsack under the tight brown skirt and in her remarkably small delicate cream ears her round pearl drop earrings trembled like young white cherries.

THE DARLING BUDS OF MAY

BUT THE night still had yet another surprise for me. When I got back to the dance floor and found Christie again I said:

'It's a simply marvellous warm night. Should we walk home across the meadows?'

'But it must be all of two miles.'

'There's a footpath. It comes out at that old stone bridge. I know the way. How did the waltz go?'

'Lovely. You weren't jealous, were you, because I danced with George?'

'Not a scrap.'

For fully a quarter of a minute those large golden eyes of hers held me in gentle and slightly mocking reproach.

'That, I think,' she said, 'was not very flattering.'

I apologized and said that, of course, it wasn't. Typically thoughtless of me.

'I wouldn't have said you were thoughtless.'

'Oh! well, it doesn't matter. Shall we walk back across the meadows?'

'If you think you know the way.'

'We'll navigate by the stars.'

As it turned out it wasn't necessary, as we started to walk home just after midnight, to navigate by the stars. The footpath was clear in the light of them. As we walked I put my arm round her waist, my hand under her right breast. We didn't talk very much but after about five minutes, half way across the first meadow, I stopped and kissed her.

In my mistaken belief that she was, after all, unimpassioned, a mere girlish meringue at once cool and sweet, I made the kiss of, as I thought, appropriate lightness. To my infinite surprise she responded with an amazing and mature tenacity, at the same time lifting one of my hands deliberately to her breast. An instant later I was suddenly aware that she was all vibration. I began trembling myself and all of a sudden, in a dynamically charged moment that even Tina couldn't have matched, we half-fell, half-stumbled to the ground.

How long we lay there I haven't the remotest idea; but some long time later she extracted herself from my embrace and then folded her body like a big warm quilt over mine, her bare breasts against my face.

'I have,' she said, 'something to tell you.'

'Oh! God, not now. Words, words – please – not words.'

'I've been wanting to tell you all evening but I didn't want to spoil it.'

'Spoil it! And you choose a moment like this. God, is it so important?'

'Of course it is. Otherwise I wouldn't tell you. Listen.'

'You expect a man to listen in an attitude like this?'

'Listen.'

It isn't all that easy to listen, rationally at any rate, when you are being held in a dark meadow, on a warm May night, by a lioness you hitherto thought was tame and is now disturbingly, passionately transfigured; but somehow, in that whirl of emotion, I listened and I heard her say:

'I'm going away.'

'What a moment to tell me!'

'Don't sound so tragic.'

'But where? You mean for good?'

She suddenly laughed gaily, in the true Davenport way, and said:

'Oh! good gracious, no. Just for a couple of weeks. On holiday. Liz Davidson has an aunt who keeps a boarding house down at Brighton. You know Liz – she works with me. We can stay for practically nothing – it's too good to miss – '

'Oh! Christie, don't go, don't go. For God's sake don't go. Not after this.'

'Of course I shall go.'

'God,' I said, 'I'll hate you if you go.'

An instant later she was on her feet, hands furiously struggling to straighten the front of her dress. It was the first and only time I ever saw her in a temper, almost a rage, and I was just preparing myself for a blast of words that would banish me for ever when suddenly her hand accidentally caught at her necklace. The string broke. There was a little explosive tinkle as the pearls scattered over her bare breasts and down the primrose dance frock, both inside and outside, to the grass below.

A moment later we were lying on the ground again, helpless with laughter.

THE FOUR BEAUTIES

'SHALL WE have breakfast in the garden, darling? It's so beautiful. The first real summer day.'

'Of course, darling. Splendid idea.'

'Good, I'll tell Grace to set it up on the lawn. And darling, did you notice that the first flower is out on the *Gloire de Dijon*?'

'No, in fact I hadn't. Isn't it awfully early, darling?'

'Not really, darling. It's almost always the first rose, that one.'

'Is it? Well, you're the observant one. That's your field.'

'I'll tell you what, darling. I'll go out and cut it and we'll have it on the breakfast table.'

'No, I'll go and cut it, darling.'

'But darling, you don't know where it is.'

'Then I'll find it, darling. Voyage of discovery.'

THE YELLOW MEADS OF ASPHODEL

42

IT IS not until the first warm late May morning, after heavy rain, that the water of the lake begins to have the true green darkness of summer. It lies still in the sun, and the first yellow water-lily buds are rigid above it, like golden drumsticks. All over the olive-emerald lily-leaves the rain of the night is caught in drops of quicksilver, and the grasses of the bank are drenched with it. The tobacco-brown tassels of reed flowers are saturated and hang down like over-ripe ears of dark water-corn. The field of beans beyond the lake path is a beautiful moist grey up the slope of land that lies in the sun, and the white and pink flowers, spitted with black, begin to be luminous and fragrant as the heat rises in the blue-white sky.

IN THE HEART OF THE COUNTRY

43

ONE EVENING in May she walked farther down the hillside than usual. It was already daylight at that time until after ten o'clock. The air after a long warm day had exceptional softness. Big white trees of hawthorn lay dotted about the valley like soft swollen puff-balls and from over the crest of the hillside, from the depths of the beech-woods, flowed a continual exquisite breath of great lakes of bluebells in flower. The war seemed a million miles away.

THE TRIPLE ECHO

OUTSIDE HE walked some distance before realizing how warm and beautiful the evening was: that the oaks, merely sprigged with buds a week ago, were now in full flower, lovely tasselled curtains of olive-yellow, already browned at the tips by the great burst of sun. All among them, too, down the road, big hawthorns were in solid pillowy white blossom, and he could smell the heavy vanilla fragrance of them as it weighted the warm wind. Spring seemed suddenly to have rushed forward, too warm, too leaf-rich, too flowery, out of the cold tight distances of a week ago. Luxuriantly the tender and dark, the sharp and misty shades of green had been kindled down the little valley, alder with beech, oak over hornbeam, all along the river and all across the wide tree-broken park to the line of white-cliffed hills that flared with miles of beeches.

He could not decide for some moments which way to go home. He stopped, looking for a little while at the country about him, the green spring world that seemed to be nothing but a series of wonderful fires of green and white quivering under the blue May sky.

He decided at last to go by the river. He had permanently locked the gates to the park some time ago. He carried the key of course: but the other way, by the small white bridge, where the river flowed shallow and bright through tunnels of purple alder and then into and out of a long, lily-padded lake, was very beautiful.

THE GRASS GOD

44

IN A gap beyond the chestnuts, where army hovels had been demo-
lished to earth level, there was a place from which you could look
down on the entire green circumference of parkland. It was so vast that
it was like a kingdom of virgin grass. A few buildings, his new
cowsheds, white concrete with green roofs of an excellent new material he had discovered, could be seen on the far edge; a slightly discordant
touch which summer, the great world of leaves, would presently
conceal.

He stopped and, leaning on the iron fence, looked down on it. A
nightingale was singing somewhere in the direction of the big empty
house, but he was so absorbed by that long deep view, the sheep-
grazed kingdom, the grass coming to lushness under hot May sun that
the singing, the sweetness, seemed only a secondary matter.

Making signals with his hat, he began explaining things to her: 'You
see we have everything under a system. Nothing haphazard. There are
five-year leys and three-year leys and one by one we plough them in
and then sow again. Grass is the key –' He broke off and looked at her.
'Boring you? I'm afraid grass is my pet thing. Sort of bible with me –'

THE GRASS GOD

SUMMER

AFTER THE long wet winter and the dark vicious spring, with days of April and May as cruel as January, summer suddenly pretends to unfold itself in a single day of cloud-cleared sky and softening wind. The morning is cool and fresh, with slow-rolling pillows of pure white cloud. At first they thicken, breezily, with under-shadows of bluish-grey, and then noon seems to lift them up, blowing them gently apart until presently they are like high flying feathers, and then by afternoon like long combed-out strands of sparse white hair, stretching transparently far across blue sky. Our horizons here, because of trees and the rolling nature of the land, are never wide: we cannot see the long westerly sweep of weald, with its sea-borne storms and fire-golden sunsets, because of high folds of beeches on the collar of a hill. But on a day like this, with a sky always lifting until it is really lofty and far away by late afternoon, the horizon itself gives the illusion of widening, creating a sense of gentle expansiveness, to which some reflection of sunlight gives a wonderful air of clarity. By afternoon too the wind stills down, and the air, warming every moment, becomes in a curious way hollow rather than quiet, a sort of glass bell in which the voices of birds keep up a high sustained vibration of echoing sweetness, a thing especially true of stuttering cuckoos and the deep round-blown notes of blackbirds.

THE COUNTRY OF WHITE CLOVER

BY THE beginning of June the weather had settled again. After the late wet spring the drying silt of the valley began to feed the grasses. All the meadows became white with sweeps of moon-daisies that were like repeated milky-ways. In the upper brooks, in iron-red marshes, cresses grew rapidly, dark and thick, and hawthorn turned pale pink and scattered itself on streams that were presently half-hidden in elder-flower and honeysuckle and arches of rose.

THE FEAST OF JULY

IT WAS when they climbed slowly up the long wide hill, already white
with the dust of early summer, that he became aware of the beans in
flower and the skylarks singing so loftily above them. The scent of
beans came in soft waves of wonderful sweetness. He saw the flowers
on the grey sunlit stalks like swarms of white, dark-throated bees. The
hawthorn flower was nearly over and was turning pink wherever it
remained. The singing of the skylarks lifted the sky upward, farther
and farther, loftier and loftier, and the sun made the blue of it clear and
blinding. He felt that all summer was pouring down the hill, between
ditches of rising meadowsweet, to meet him. The cold quivering days
of coltsfoot flower, the icy-sunny days of racing cloud-shadow over
drying ploughland, the dark-white days of April hail, were all behind
him, and he was thirsty with summer dust and his face was hot in the
sun.

THE WATERCRESS GIRL

HER FIRST sight of the river at the street-end, where the last houses suddenly plunged down a narrow hill that was blocked at the foot by a gated hump-backed bridge, did not surprise her. She was still not capable of surprise. She saw beyond the bridge, spanned over the deep summer-dark water like a big arching brown-red cat, the beginning of the countryside. Wide meadows repeated themselves, all pasture, far across the valley, to a sky-line of spare elms a mile or two beyond. By that time of year all the cattle had been taken up from the meadows. The deep flood-silt of winter had fed the grasses so that now the entire valley lay like a vast lake-bed of grass, thick and rich, stirring and waving in the sun with soft brushes of pale gold seed.

THE FEAST OF JULY

ROSIE PERKINS, up at five, dressing at the bedroom window, looked beyond the river flowing past the pub-yard and across the hay-meadows extending beyond the river as far as she could see. The little summer mists still hanging in the low places like wisps of hay themselves were the same cloud-colour as the water. She was so dizzy with sleep that the river, flowing heavily after the storm, seemed as she looked at it to surge gently up and down like a sea, little back-washing waves slapping the mud of the tow path bank on one side and the stones of the pub wall on the other. A sight of hay was out, drenched, more than she had ever seen, and the feeling of thunder was still everywhere. The air in the room drugged her.

A HOUSE OF WOMEN

It was summer. The hot, still days were followed by evenings of a lovely sultry peacefulness scented with mown hay, dog-roses and clover. The river, day and night, looked as if it slept between its rows of still, luscious green reeds.

FISHING

51

THE WEEK of his leave went past. Neither of them spoke again about a bus, a train, a moment of departure. For seven whole days he became as complete a part of the little farm as the cow, the tractor, the sheep grazing on the thin pasture below yellow fringes of rock roses beginning now to bloom on the hot exposed ridge of chalk.

It was now June. Some of the passion had gone from the first frenzied singing of nightingales but on the final evening of his leave the two of them walked to the edge of the beechwood, to listen through a darkening evening of tense clear air for some occasional suspended string of song.

THE TRIPLE ECHO

AFTER THAT she began to go up to the farm every evening. With the money Parker gave her she bought the material for the curtains and made them and hung them up. They were of bright yellow material, with scrolling scarlet roses, and they flapped like signal flags against the windows of the square drab house on the hill. As summer came on she cleaned through the sitting-room, the stairs and the landing, and then into the three bedrooms above. Parker had slept in a small back bedroom on an iron bedstead, throwing an old army overcoat over himself for extra warmth in winter. She turned him out of this frowsy unwashed room into another and then out of that into another, until the three were cleaned. She beat the dust from the carpets in the farmyard and washed the sheets until they too looked like long rows of signal flags strung out under the summer apple-trees.

From time to time Parker said 'I shall atta settle for your time,' or 'Soon as I git that hayin' done I'll settle up wi' you,' but on all these occasions she would simply look at him with her slow dark eyes, as if searching for something beyond him, and say:

'It don't matter. There's no hurry, Mr Parker. There's plenty of time.'

Summer was dry and beautiful on the hill and in the evenings, from that high point about the farm, the sun seemed to go down very slowly across the plain of deep flat country below. Because of this she got into the habit of waiting for Parker to come in from the fields, no matter how late it was. Now that the rooms were all turned out and tidy it was easier to keep everything clean and sometimes there was nothing to do but lay the table for supper.

DULCIMA

IN THE midday heat of a June day a farm-boy was riding down a deserted meadow-lane, straddling a fat white pony. The blossoms of hawthorn had shrivelled to brown on the tall hedges flanking the lane and wild pink and white roses were beginning to open like stars among the thick green leaves. The air was heavy with the scent of early summer, the odour of the dying hawthorn bloom, the perfume of the dog-roses, the breath of ripening grass.

The boy had taken off his jacket and had hooked it over the straw victual-bag hanging from the saddle. There were bottles of beer in the bag and the jacket shaded them from the heat of the sun. The pony moved at walking-pace and the boy rode cautiously, never letting it break into a trot. As though it was necessary to be careful with the beer, he sometimes halted the pony and touched the necks of the bottles with his fingers. The bottlenecks were cool, but the cloth of his jacket was burning against his hand.

He presently steered the pony through a white gate leading from the lane to a meadow beyond. The gate was standing open and he rode the pony straight across the curving swathes of hay which lay drying in the

sun. It was a field of seven or eight acres and a third of the grass had already been mown. The hay was crisp and dry under the pony's feet and the flowers that had been growing in the grass lay white and shrivelled in the sunshine.

Over on the far side of the field a man was mowing and a woman was turning the rows of grass with a hay rake. The figure of the man was nondescript and dark, and the woman was dressed in a white blouse and an old green skirt that had faded to the yellowish colour of the grass the man was mowing. The boy rode the pony towards them. The sunshine blazed down fierce and perpendicular, and there was no shade in the field except for the shadow of an ash tree in one corner and a group of willows by a cattle-pond in another.

Everywhere was silence and the soft sound of the pony's feet in the hay and the droning of bees in the flowers among the uncut grass seemed to deepen the silence.

THE MOWER

OUTSIDE, BEYOND the sun-bathed balcony, he could hear summer growing in the evening voices of droning pigeons and in the throaty sweetness of several blackbirds in woods along the river. Bees were still working, perhaps on a tree of roses, just beyond the window, on the house wall. He could feel all summer growing and deepening in those sounds. He could feel it in the turn of her body, in the flame of butterfly wings darting yellow across the sun. He could even feel it in a curious softening and mounting ache in his own limbs. It was mounting and deepening and richening everywhere, rapidly and luxuriantly, with his own miles and miles of grass.

'I've a feeling the summer is going to be wonderful,' he said. 'Wonderful fun.'

'I think so too,' she said.

THE GRASS GOD

55

ONCE IN the summer time, when the water-lilies were in bloom and the wheat was new in ear, his grandfather took him on a long walk up the river, to see his Uncle Crow. He had heard so much of Uncle Crow, so much that was wonderful and to be marvelled at, and for such a long time, that he knew him to be, even before that, the most remarkable fisherman in the world.

'Masterpiece of a man, your Uncle Crow,' his grandfather said. 'He could git a clothes-line any day and tie a brick on it and a mossel of cake and go out and catch a pike as long as your arm.'

When he asked what kind of cake his grandfather seemed irritated and said it was just like a boy to ask questions of that sort.

'Any kind o' cake,' he said. 'Plum cake. Does it matter? Carraway cake. Christmas cake if you like. Anything. I shouldn't wonder if he could catch a pretty fair pike with a cold baked tater.'

'Only a pike?'

'Times,' his grandfather said, 'I've seen him sittin' on the bank on a sweltering hot day like a furnace, when nobody was gittin' a bite not even off a bloodsucker. And there your Uncle Crow'd be a-pullin' 'em but by the dozen, like a man shellin' harvest beans.'

GREAT UNCLE CROW

ALWAYS THE air in June seems to have been clotted with the intoxication of mown grass, of may-blossom, of moon-daisies dying along the paling swathes.

THE VANISHED WORLD

IT WAS certainly, people were saying, the most wonderful summer for years. This, they said, was what you called a summer. You knew, with such a summer, where you were. Day unfolded after day, hot and tranquil, settled under blue soft skies, into distances shortened and trembling under heat haze. In the garden a rapid luxuriance of nettle and thistle and yellow ragwort sprang up, with thickets of wild rose and frothy elder, to choke what had once been paths and beds and lawns between the crumbling walls. On the house the snow-broken magnolia lifted immense copper-green leaves centrally filled by buds of solid waxy cream. A pale bluish fire sprang from the tips of cedar branches. Across the park the great limes were early in flower and down across the meadows the hay was early too.

THE GRASS GOD

HE POURED himself half a tumbler of whisky and took it into the garden. Scarlet beans, budded low down with sprays of flower, were already curling far up a row of hazel sticks beyond the flower beds. He could see a great difference in them, as in everything else, since yesterday. Swallows were flying high in the warm air above the house, crying thinly, and on the single-storeyed wall beyond the dining-room, where there had once been only pigsties and a filthy little copper-house for boiling potatoes one day and washing the next, the new *Gloire de Dijon* rose was already in bloom, its fat flowers like stirred cream in the evening sun.

He had converted the pigsties into a sort of loggia and summer-house. Everything had been done very tastefully; and now it was not possible to believe that there, where the rose flowered and where big pots of blue agapanthus lily would bloom all summer, the hideous pigsties had ever existed or that a family of half-gipsies had lived in care-free squalor in the rest of the house. It showed what could be done.

Walking about the garden, looking at the climbing beans, the roses that had rushed into bloom in a day, the blue and orange steeples of lupins, he felt once again that summer was overflowing too fast, rising like a warm and delicious torrent. He felt he wanted to hold it up, to make it permanent where it rose, before all the tender and dark and fiery greenness deepened into solid June.

THE GRASS GOD

THEY WALKED on into the high country beyond the town. The land went sweeping away before them with a splendour of distance, the pattern of fields and woods clear and bright in the sharp sunlight to the very edge of the horizon, the infinite summer greenness of it broken by the endless blossoming of hawthorn, like soft gigantic, fluffy knots of whiteness in the nearest fields, then like some faint feather-stitching on the hedges far away. There were fields of buttercups, riotous with bright gold, which they would stay to gaze on in long, amazed silences.

CHARLOTTE'S ROW

AFTER QUENCHING his thirst with a steady quart of shandy at The Hare and Hounds Pop arrived home in the expectation of finding Ma in the kitchen, surrounded as always by dishes, saucepans, and piles of food. His eager mating call of 'Hullo, hullo, where's my old sunflower?' remained, however, unanswered; and it was some minutes before he discovered her in the garden, where she had set up easel, canvas, paint box and camp stool and was busy painting a picture of Mariette in the nude. She seemed fatter and rounder than ever, sitting on the tiny camp stool.

When she saw Pop crossing the garden Mariette deftly but with otherwise no great concern, covered her resplendent and now maternal nakedness with the *Daily Mirror*, which in turn linked up with the only garment she was wearing, a pair of transparent purple briefs with lace edges. Having given birth two months before to a boy who, at Ma's suggestion, had been named John Marlborough Churchill Blenheim Charlton, she was now anxious to coax her figure back to its normal splendid proportions and to get it, if possible, brown all over. The result was that Ma was now doing a different picture of her almost every other day, either from the front, the back or the sides, according to which part of her was most in the need of being sun-tanned. Mr

Charlton found the canvases of intense and palpitating interest, so much so that he had had two of them, one a full-blooded frontal view, the other a horizontal back view of Mariette lying among buttercups, framed.

'Hullo, hullo,' Pop said. 'Art class? Very nice too. How's it coming on?'

Looking over Ma's shoulder he surveyed, with something more than paternal pride, the stunning contours of Mariette's upper figure as seen by Ma. It was six months since Ma had taken up painting, largely because practically everyone else, from Churchill downwards, had taken it up too. She was surprisingly good at it, everyone thought. She had also read the great man's little book on the subject and as well as being inspired to name the new baby after him had also taken his advice to revel in paint as a physical luxury.

'Bit blue, ain't they, Ma?'

Greatly though he admired Ma's newly revealed talents, there were times when he thought she might be going a bit too modern. The splendour of Mariette's upper contours looked, he thought, not only as blue as cornflowers but also a bit lop-sided somehow, but he supposed it all depended on how you looked at them. The artist's eye and all that.

'Well, they're no bluer that you'll be if you don't soon make yourself scarce so's I can get another look at them. Go and get yourself a drink, do. I can't very well see through the *Daily Mirror*, can I?'

Pop cordially agreed, at the same time blandly suggesting that he himself had no objection if Mariette wanted to take the *Daily Mirror* away. What did it matter? It was all one to him. It was all in the family.

'By the way,' Mariette said, 'there's some letters for you. One of them with a foreign stamp on.'

'That's it,' Ma said, 'go and read your letters. And bring us both a decent cold drink when you come back. It's hot out here in the sun.'

OH! TO BE IN ENGLAND

61

As Pop Larkin loaded the last pieces of junk into his newly-painted yellow-and-scarlet pick-up all the essence of the fine June morning seemed to pour down like dreamy honey from thick boughs of oak-flower, gold-green against a sky of purest blue, unblemished except for a few floating white doves of cloud. It was a morning when he felt it was good to be alive; you could fairly hear the grass growing. All the air was brilliant with bird song and farther up the road, on a little rise, a field thick with buttercups shone brighter than a bank of sovereigns.

OH! TO BE IN ENGLAND

ON THE first day they walked to Pollards' Mill she did not talk much. The weather was warm and breathless. At first she was not quite certain of the way and gradually the path lost itself, overgrown with elder and hawthorn and big savage wands of dog-rose coming into flower.

Then suddenly there was no path. Only, beyond a broken gate, the oasis of the mill: the windowless stone house with elder foaming at door-gaps, sluice-gates rotten, mill-pond ringed with high dark reeds and over everything the hot baked smell of marsh-earth drying in sun.

She stopped and looked at it. 'This is the place,' she said.

Most of that afternoon, their first visit, they lay above the sluice, watching the water. A few small fish were basking in the sun. A dull skin stretched across the pool, with only occasional small water-beetles rowing paths across it.

She turned to say something and saw him lying with his face to the sky. Across the pool a sudden scuttle of light wind travelled like a shoal of rising fish. She saw it lift his hair. Then it rose and blew into her face, lifting her own hair and brushing down her body.

As she felt the wind blowing softly on her the needs and feelings of her body began waking. It was like an artery that had been tied and suddenly released again. Blood began pouring and racing back, with sensations of sharper, brighter pain.

After a moment he turned his face too and they were looking at each other. The vivid pale blue eyes were transparent, almost colourless, in the sun. She looked at them for almost a minute, completely trans-fixed, in wonder.

Then he was touching her. He held her quietly and lightly with his fingers, on her bare upper arms. She could not move. She felt the wind quiver from the pond again, disturbing her skirt. For some moments she let it blow on her legs and body and then her skirt lifted again and she moved her hands, trying to smooth it down.

Suddenly they lay against each other in an agony of kissing. She found herself holding his mouth in pure bright pain. In the hot silence she could hear nothing but the occasional dreamy croak of moorhens lost in reeds and a sudden quiver of wind in willow-leaves above the pond.

SLEEPLESS MOON

THERE WERE no nests in the spinney except a pigeon's high up in a hazel-tree that was too thin to climb. He was not quite sure about the song of a nightingale. He knew the blackbird's, full and rich and dark like the bird itself and deep like the summer shadow of the closing wood, and with the voices of thrushes the blackbirds' song filled all the wood with bell-sounds and belling echoes.

Beyond the wood the day was clear and hot. The grass was high to his knees and the ground, falling away, was marshy in places, with mounds of sedge, as it ran down towards the back-brook and the river. He walked with his eyes on the ground, partly because of oozy holes among the sedge, partly because he hoped to see the brown ring of a moorhen's nest in the marshier places.

It was because of his way of walking that he did not see, for some time, a girl standing up to her knees in red-ochre mud, among half-floating beds of dark-green cresses. But suddenly he lifted his head and saw her standing there, bare-legged and bare-armed, staring at him as if she had been watching him for a long time. Her brown osier cress-basket was like a two-bushel measure and was slung over her shoulder with a strap.

'You don't live here,' she said.

'No,' he said. 'Do you?'

'Over there,' she said. 'In that house.'

'Which house?' He could not see a house.

'You come here and you can see it,' she said.

When he had picked his way through tufts of sedge to where she was standing in the bed of cresses he still could not see a house, either about the wood or across the meadows on the rising ground beyond.

'You can see the chimney smoking,' she said.

'It's not a house. It's a hut,' he said.

'That's where we live.'

'All the time?'

'Yes,' she said. 'You're sinking in.'

The toes of his boots were slowly drowning in red-ochre water.

'If you're coming out here you'd better take your shoes and stockings off,' she said.

64

A moment or two later his bare feet were cool in the water. She was gathering cresses quickly, cutting them off with an old shoe-knife, leaving young sprigs and trailing skeins of white root behind. She was older than himself, nine or ten, he thought, and her hair hung ribbonless and uncombed, a brown colour, rather like the colour of the basket, down her back.

'Can I gather?' he said, and she said, yes, if he knew what brook-lime was.

'I know brook-lime,' he said. 'Everybody knows brook-lime.'

'Then which is it? Show me which it is. Which is brook-lime?'

That was almost as bad, he thought, as being nagged by Sar' Ann. The idea that he did not know brook-lime from cress seemed to him a terrible insult and a pain. He snatched up a piece in irritation but it did not break and came up instead from the mud-depths in a long rope of dripping red-black slime, spattering his shirt and trousers.

She laughed at this and he laughed too. Her voice, he thought, sounded cracked, as if she were hoarse from shouting or a cold. The sound of it carried a long way. He heard it crack over the meadows and the river with a coarse broken sort of screech that was like the slitting of rag in the deep oppressive afternoon.

He never knew till long afterwards how much he liked that sound. She repeated it several times during the afternoon. In the same cracked voice she laughed at questions he asked or things he did not know. In places the water, shallower, was warm on his feet, and the cresses were a dark polished green in the sun. She laughed because he did not know that anyone could live by gathering cresses. He must be a real town boy, she said. There was only she and her father, she told him, and she began to tell what he afterwards knew were beautiful lies about the way they got up every other day at two in the morning and tramped out to sell cresses in Evensford and Bedford and towns about the valley.

'But the shops aren't open then,' he said and that made her laugh again, cracked and thin, with that long slitting echo across the drowsy meadows.

'It's not in the shops we sell them,' she said. 'It's in the streets – don't you know that? – in the streets – '

And suddenly she lifted her head and drew back her throat and yelled the cry she used in the streets. He had heard that cry before, high and long and melancholy, like a call across lonely winter marshes in its slow fall and dying away, and there was to be a time in his life when it died for ever and he never heard it again:

'Watercree-ee-ee-ee-ee-s! Fresh cre-ee-ee-ee-ee-ee-s! Lovely fresh watercre-ee-ee-ee-ee-ee-s!'

Standing up to his knees in water, his hands full of wet cresses and slimy skeins of roots dripping red mud down his shirt and trousers, he listened to that fascinating sound travelling like a bird-cry, watery and not quite earthly, down through the spinney and the meadows of buttercup and the places where the pike were supposed to lie.

His eyes must have been enormous and transfixed in his head as he listened, because suddenly she broke the note of the cry and laughed at him again and then said:

'You do it. You see if you can do it –'

What came out of his mouth was like a little soprano trill compared

66

with her own full-throated, long-carrying cry. It made her laugh again and she said:

'You ought to come with us. Come with us tomorrow – how long are you staying here?'

'Only today.'

'I don't know where we'll go tomorrow,' she said. 'Evensford, I think. Sometimes we go forty or fifty miles – miles and miles. We go to Buckingham market sometimes – that's forty miles–'

'Evensford,' he said. 'That's where I come from. I could see you there if you go.'

'All right,' she said. 'Where will you be? We come in by *The Waggon and Horses* – down the hill, that way.'

'I'll be at *The Waggon and Horses* waiting for you,' he said. 'What time?'

'You be there at five o'clock,' she said. 'Then I'll learn you how to do it, like this – watercree-ee-ee-ee-ee-ee-ee-s! Fresh cree-ee-ee-ee-ee-ee-ee-s! Lovely fresh watercree-ee-ee-ee-ee-s!'

THE WATERCRESS GIRL

THE GARDEN was a wilderness of trees and sweet-briar, untidy holly-hocks with shabby pink buttons just unfolding, blood-bright poppies that had sown themselves in thousands about the flower-beds and the paths and on the front door-step itself. The air seemed sleepy with poppy odour. The brilliant scarlet heads blazed like signals of danger.

INNOCENCE

ACROSS THE meadow lying between junk-yard and river Jasmine Brown walked deep in buttercups, her half-naked breasts thrust forward like those of some stately figurehead, her bare feet bright yellow with pollen. Once she started running and the rear view of her, its curves firmly marked and yet quivering, was of so sensational a substance that the Captain actually halted in his stride. It was only when she suddenly stopped, turned and held out both arms to him as if he were the only person in the world that he was prompted to move again.

'Come on! Race you, Colonel, race you!'

In puffing pursuit, the Captain caught her up at the boat-house, where Pop's new golden row-boat lay side by side with its sister status symbol, the motor-boat, both resplendent with purple and yellow cushions.

Stripping off his jacket, the Captain told himself that this was really where he came in. He could really show some prowess now. With a strong arm he held the boat steady while Jasmine Brown climbed in. Her body, if sensational on the stairs, was now positively volcanic in its unsparing beauty as she lay full length, every curve and coutour tautly revealed, on the brilliant cushions.

The Captain got into the boat too and rowed out into a stream just wide enough at that point to take his oars. The surface of the river, broken here and there by small islands of water lilies just coming into flower, was sometimes rippled by the gentlest breath of air. Now and then a leaf of yellow flag-iris twisted on the banks. A swallow or two occasionally came low over the stream, piercing the air with voices of needling excitement, but these, except for the level slip of the oars, were the only sounds.

By Jove, this, the Captain let it be known, was rather good.

'Absolute heaven.' Jasmine Brown, cool but radiating that same sensational heat of which Pop had taken such good notice, stared up at him with eyes that seemed to fill with a deep entrancement of wonder. 'You row beautifully.'

The Captain was sure that he did.

'After all I used to stroke —'

'Stroke?'

The single word seemed to be caress, flattery and invitation all in one. She raised her arms and clasped them together behind a head almost too beautiful in its frame of black hair. This gesture too seemed to be open invitation but the Captain made no sign of accepting it, and merely made steady progress with the oars. Like a cat snuggling down to half-sleep she then nestled even lower into the cushions, the soft underparts of her arms quivering, and held him with blissful, predatory, drowsy eyes.

'Come on. Do I have to drag you down here? You bring a girl out in a boat and then do absolutely nothing about it.'

The Captain, though half-terrified, could resist no longer. With nervous hands he shipped oars, stood up precariously and then half-sat, half-knelt on the cushions beside her.

The boat rocked. At the same moment Jasmine Brown seized him in an embrace as fierce and all-enfolding as that of a lioness overcoming its prey. Her splendid frame encompassed him completely. The boat rocked again and the Captain, half-suffocated, uttered a stifled shout. Her lips smothered his own with a passion so well simulated that he actually found himself struggling against it and then the boat rocked a third time, this time with violence, dangerously.

A moment later the Captain, flamboyant as a tailor's dummy, flopped helplessly overboard and Jasmine Brown fell with him, shrieking with splendid laughter.

OH! TO BE IN ENGLAND

ON A midsummer night of that same year, 1896, he saw Spella Ho illuminated as he had wanted to see it: fairy lights in blue, crimson and gold piped along the terrace and on the flat stone face of the house; inside the house an elaborate brass system of chandeliers and brackets, on the stairs a great blaze of uprights, like candles, lighting up magnificently the dim cherubim and seraphim on the ceiling above. The house and gardens and park were thrown open to the public and were crowded; the lake like some miniature sea on a Bank Holiday: fairy lights piped among the embroidery of trees along the water-edge, the water oar-rippled and rainbow coloured, shining as oil. And all the time, a background to the noise of voices, a quiet hissing of gas, drowned finally by the string-band on the terrace, the Strauss waltzes, the laughter, the shuffle and swish of feet and skirts dancing on lawn and stone. He stood on the terrace and made a speech, his crude strong voice like a tear in the plush fabric of the evening, and felt it to be the supreme moment of his life: the gas, the crowds, the toffs, himself rubbing elbows with people of class, talking to them, explaining things, moving among them at last as a man to be reckoned with. It was a triumph for himself and Preston, who alone knew what it had cost in energy, time, money and courage. He walked about rather like the manager of some elaborate vaudeville show, wearing his first top hat with an ordinary suit, his cuffs slipping down, his huge body mocking the slight dandyism of tight white waistcoat and steep collar. He looked and felt immensely proud of himself walking about there in the glow of his own gaslight, like some large ape that had learned to do its tricks at last.

SPELLA HO

70

SOMETIMES, WHEN the evenings were fine and warm, they didn't even bother with the formality of a meal. She would make sandwiches, he would bring a bottle of wine and then they would wander across the Common, across stretches of heather and asphodel now in pink and yellow flower, until they found some dry, secluded place to picnic. When the food and wine were both finished they lay down together in long and often completely silent embrace, exchanging long, all-consuming kisses or simply staring up at the sky until the first specks of stars began to break the twilight.

THE YELLOW MEADS OF ASPHODEL

I<small>T IS</small> Midsummer Day in the year 1941, the air so quiet and warm in the early morning that you can hear the voice of someone shouting orders to a platoon of soldiers beyond the woods four or five miles away. A little breeze has sprung up in the night. Yellow leaves now and then shake down from the willow-trees, and with them a sprinkle of cotton seed. Savage scarlet stalks of poppy and cool white wands of foxglove are blooming against the apple-trees. The birds are already quiet, but you can hear now and then the greedy, quibbling voice of a young cuckoo, fresh flown from a nest of hedge-sparrows, where he has been fed for a fortnight at the rate of five or six hundred meals a day. For a short time there was the sound also of someone driving wedges into cordwood across the road, but now that has stopped, and the only persistent and continuous sound besides the light sound of wind in summer leaves is the sound of bees working the grey-violet catmint flowers, where the black cat already lies asleep in the sun.

I<small>N THE</small> H<small>EART OF THE</small> C<small>OUNTRY</small>

S<small>HE WENT</small> up another flight of steps on to the roof above. A square balustraded platform had been built there by some previous owner who had evidently wanted the air, the stars, the sun or simply the long view, across twenty miles of valley, to the sea.

She stood for some time fascinated by this view. It opened out a world that lay below her like a map. She could see not only the fields she knew, bare and white after the heat of summer and harvest, but small chalky veins of road winding away among clotted copses of sweet chestnut, through fox-red villages and fields of dark green potatoes. She could see, five or six miles away, the square stone church tower of the market town and then, far beyond it, delicate and faint, the line of sea horizon, with a few creeping charcoal puffs that were the smoke of passing steamers. It created for her the curious and heady illusion that here, above everything, alone and on top of the world, she had never been able to see so far.

DULCIMA

ALMOST UNCONSCIOUSLY she stood drawing her hands up and down the flanks of her body. She could feel the straight hard bones of her thighs and the stony edges of her hips, both graceless, almost without flesh. Through the open upper sash of the window the night air of late June was still and hot, without wind, and from somewhere, delicately, was borne the first scent of hay. She did not know how long she breathed this scent without noticing it. It might have been for ten minutes or so. Then she was not only aware of it but she was aware of it waking her. She began to recall, because of it, the way she had let herself be rowed on the river. She remembered the swans, the huge white pools of daisies starry in high meadow grass, the rise and fall of fish and the immense hot after-glow of midsummer on the far westerly crest of the valley. She had forgotten that there were such things.

THE FEAST OF JULY

73

THEY WERE to meet at eleven, when the church-bell had finished, and they were to go back to the farm for tea. The morning was hot and brilliant. The path by the brook was a parched brown line, the last of the dog-roses were withering on the hedges, the grey willow leaves drooping in the heat, the birds quietening down for noon, bringing a quivering silence. Up on the hill the corn stood stiff and straight, still green, the ears unfolding from the curving sheaths, ready to swell and yellow. David had brought a peck-basket of food and his army haversack full of knives and cups and a billy-can for tea. He kept looking furtively at Anthea; her face was fresher and brighter and the sunlight had enriched the light in her eyes, and he liked her thin cotton dress with a flower pattern in it. She was carrying a small paper bag. They turned away from the stream and followed the backwater. The day quietened as they went, the water too gentle and slow to make a sound, the midsummer sky an intensely bright blue with heat. In a deep green pool a mass of water-lilies covered the whole width of the stream with snow and gold, the pale flat leaves gleaming with sunlight, the fat buds pushing up among them like cool water-roses, half-green, half-white.

Within sight of the lilies, under a big alder, they sat down and made a fire of old reeds and dry, dead wood, the smoke curling straight up through the tree to sunlight. They boiled the billy-can, full of spring water, and Anthea laid out the food he had brought. The noon silence was intense, the meadow quivering with heat, the water-lilies blazing under the perpendicular beat of the sunshine.

THE FALLOW LAND

THE SUMMER became a close and stormy one. A few days of heat would gather oppressively and then develop into strange yellow evenings of groping thunder. When the storms had broken and the sun came out again heat seemed to smoulder damply about the town and fields, sucking at air, leaving the afternoons breathless.

By July the mill-pond was partly covered with white water-lilies, over the pads of which small blue dragonflies hovered and young moorhens walked with slow daintiness, heads down, as if fascinated by the reflection of themselves in dark waters.

THE SLEEPLESS MOON

JULY COMES in with days of high-feathered cloud and hot distances and the sound of hay-mowers down the valley.

THE COUNTRY OF WHITE CLOVER

JULY CAME in hot and with great beauty. The rambler roses were rich deep crimson with fire. The big-leaved magnolia on the walls of the dove-cot began to show, much earlier than usual, its pointed buds of cream. Every day baskets of fruit came in from the gardens of the big house, strawberries, black, red and white currants, gooseberries and raspberries, and every evening Edna and Rose were in the kitchen, with me helping them, sometimes until midnight, topping and tailing gooseberries, plugging strawberries and making innumerable pots of jam and jelly, including the white-currant one, which in fact turns out in the making to be a pale pink shade.

A MOMENT IN TIME

By July the silence is beginning, and the flowerlessness. Nightingale and cuckoo have finished their season, and the month comes in full of the slumbrous broken moaning of wood-pigeons in the great canopies of sun-metallic leaves. I say broken, because it is broken, because it often ceases abruptly on a phrase and then after an interval, sometimes a long interval, begins where it left off – coo coo-coo coo-coo, coo-coo, coo-coo, coo – as though the bird were cooing itself into a constant day-sleep in the drowsy branches. Of all notes it is the note of high summer. It has in it the monotonous soothing drowsiness of a high noon. There is something in it that drugs the blood and that in turn deepens and stupefies the silence of the day. With it, the year seems to drop off into a snooze. There comes a feeling of oh! let it go, don't worry, sit still, have five minutes in the shade, let it go, a feeling that nothing matters. The climax has been reached, the year stands still.

THROUGH THE WOODS

EVERY MORNING was golden; even the First World War had not begun. The hedgerows of spring were clothed with the cream of May-blossom; those of June and July with pink and white dog-roses, meadowsweet and willow-herb. If the paradise made by it all was about to be shattered, not once but twice, I happily hadn't even the remotest suspicion of the gathering cloud. Sticklebacks were in the brook, cuckoos called from the elms, yellowhammers swooned away long summer afternoons in lanes shimmering with heat and virtually undefiled by the motor-car, and consequently all was right with the world.

THE VANISHED WORLD

THEY CAME to the river. She was suddenly astonished to see crowds of people on both banks, the stream itself full of boats, the trees festooned, long lines of little triangular flags drooping between the branches. The pale, bluish water was ruffled and eddied, full of reflections and lights of all colours, red swimming with black, green and gold. From the boats Japanese sunshades lolled and drooped. Everywhere people were laughing, talking, calling greetings and remarks to each other. Now and then someone would shout through a megaphone, like a giant disturbed, and in the brief hush a gramophone would go on playing its tune as if mocking. At one spot a band was getting ready to play, the instruments flashing brassily in the sun, the men pom-pomming and trilling before beginning. And through the trees, behind it all, still and silent in the sunshine, she now and then caught glimpses of meadows stretching far away in a picture of cool, tranquil green.

After some delay, during which she chattered much and was alternately annoyed and amused at Charles's persistent 'I hope it'll keep fine. I hope so!' they rowed off.

THE CATHERINE FOSTER

'DARE WE open the window?' she said. 'It's so hot in here.'

'I'll open the back window,' I said.

'I'm stifled – let's have some air.' She let go my hand. 'Why don't you take off your shirt? The sweat's pouring from you like water – '

The back window looked out from a tiny landing where the stairs came up. I went through to open it. Through the small casement, as I threw it back, came the heat of July, clear and fierce, sweet with light undertones of hay still being turned in fields outside the park. I stood breathing it for a moment, listening to the beat of a hay-turner, undoing the front of my shirt so that air could cool my chest.

When I went back to her she had taken off her dress. She was sitting up in the long chair, unrolling her stockings. They peeled from her thighs like another skin, leaving the flesh wonderfully white and without blemishes.

She lay back in the chair. I touched her thighs with light tips of my fingers and began to say something about how much I had wanted to touch her and how –

'I wondered if you ever would,' she said. 'If you ever wanted – '

LOVE FOR LYDIA

79

IT WAS one of those rare afternoons in July when the air was drenched in the scent of roses and the fragrance of hay lying thick-cut in field after field along the river as we drove up in the big landaulette taxi we had hired to bring us from the village station. It was very hot that day, in spite of a strong breeze, and with a remarkable shimmering light on all the distances.

This light had one extraordinary effect I shall never forget. As we drove along the road to the house we were, at one point, high above the valley on an open ridge. Below us we could see perhaps a mile of river winding in big curves, under hump-backed bridges of stone, among the rich flat fields of hay.

Suddenly I saw, repeated again and again, all along the stream, what I thought at first were flocks of pure white ducks. They seemed to be floating quite motionless, between dark green banks of reed. Then, as the taxi dropped further and further down the valley, I saw that I was mistaken. What I had thought were ducks were really whole islands, purest white, of water-lilies, in the crown of their bloom.

THE QUEEN OF SPAIN FRITILLARY

FROM THE windows of *The Three Bells* you looked across flat lands, downstream to the sea, and there were sea-fish in the estuary. Men came down from towns in the upper valley for a week or two of fishing in the summer, hiring boats from the hotel, and Arch Wilson had been one of them in July.

'Arch Wilson. I'll be coming down again in a month. I'll drop you a card when I know the day.'

In summer the wide flat lands were blue-grey with sea-thistle. She remembered how the dry spines had pricked the bare gap of her thighs above her black stockings as she lay with him there under a breezy sky.

'You know what colour your eyes are?'

'Green.' She remembered laughing easily, as she always laughed in those days, with her tongue out. 'That's every bit green you can see there.'

'They're black,' he said. 'Black as cherries. That's what they are.'

'They're green,' she said, 'all green when you talk to me.'

'I'll be back in a month and I'll bring you a pair of shoes. Low shoes. Glacé.'

'I bet you'll never be back.'

'August,' he said. 'The second week in August. What size are your feet?'

'You're a shoemaker. You ought to know.'

'God, your eyes are black,' he said and she laughed, again in the warm, easy friendly way she had in those days.

But it was really the feeling of his hands on her stockinged feet, she remembered, and then the feeling of soft fresh sea-wind on the bare skin of her legs that really woke her. She remembered beginning to tremble all over.

'Threes,' he said. 'Narrow fitting. No bigger than a doll's.'

THE FEAST OF JULY

MY GREAT-UNCLE Silas used to live in a small stone reed-thatched cottage on the edge of a pine-wood, where nightingales sang passionately in great numbers through early summer nights and on into the mornings and often still in the afternoons. On summer days after rain the air was sweetly saturated with the fragrance of the pines, which mingled subtly with the exquisite honeysuckle scent, the strange vanilla heaviness from the creamy elder-flowers in the garden hedge and the perfume of old pink and white crimped-double roses of forgotten names. It was very quiet there except for the soft, water-whispering sound of leaves and boughs, and the squabbling and singing of birds in the house-thatch and the trees. The house itself was soaked with years of scents, half-sweet, half-dimly-sour with the smell of wood smoke, the curious odour of mauve and milk-coloured and red geraniums, of old wine and tea and the earth smell of my Uncle Silas himself.

It was the sort of house to which old men retire to enjoy their last days. Shuffling about in green carpet-slippers, they do nothing but poke the fire, gloomily clip their beards, read the newspapers with their spectacles on upside down, take too much physic and die of boredom at last.

But my Uncle Silas was different. At the age of ninety-three he was as lively and restless as a young colt. He shaved every morning at half-past five with cold water and a razor older than himself which resembled an antique barbaric bill-hook. He still kept alive within him some gay, devilish spark of audacity which made him attractive to the ladies. He ate too much and he drank too much.

'God strike me if I tell a lie,' he used to say, 'but I've drunk enough beer, me boyo, to float the fleet and a drop over.'

I remember seeing him on a scorching, windless day in July. He ought to have been asleep in the shade with his red handkerchief over his old walnut-coloured face, but when I arrived he was at work on his potato-patch, digging steadily and strongly in the full blaze of the sun.

Hearing the click of the gate he looked up, and seeing me, waved his spade. The potato-patch was at the far end of the long garden, where the earth was warmest under the woodside, and I walked down the

long path to it between rows of fat-podded peas and beans and full-fruited bushes of currant and gooseberry. By the house, under the sun-white wall, the sweet-williams and white pinks flamed softly against the hot marigolds and the orange poppies flat opened to drink in the sun.

'Hot,' I said.

'Warmish.' He did not pause in his strong, rhythmical digging. The potato-patch had been cleared of its crop and the sun-withered haulms had been heaped against the hedge.

'Peas?' I said. The conversation was inevitably laconic.

'Taters,' he said. He did not speak again until he had dug to the edge of the wood. There he straightened his back, blew his nose on his red handkerchief, let out a nonchalant flash of spittle, and cocked his eye at me.

'Two crops,' he said. 'Two crops from one bit o' land. How's that, me boyo? Every heard talk o' that?'

'Never.'

'And you'd be telling a lie if you said you had. Because I know you ain't.'

He winked at me, with that swift cock of the head and the perky flicker of the lid that had in it all the saucy jauntiness of a youth of twenty. He was very proud of himself. He was doing something extraordinary and he knew it. There was no humbug about him.

Sitting in the low shade of the garden hedge I watched him, waiting for him to finish digging. He was a short, thick-built man, and his old corduroy trousers concertina-folded over his squat legs and his old wine-red waistcoat ruckled up over his heavy chest made him look dwarfer and thicker still. He was as ugly as some old Indian idol, his skin walnut-stained and scarred like a weather-cracked apple, his cheeks hanging loose and withered, his lips wet and almost sensual and a trifle sardonic with their sideways twist and the thick pout of the lower lip. His left eye was bloodshot, a thin vein or two of scarlet staining the white, but he kept the lid half-shut, only raising it abruptly now and then with an odd cocking-flicker that made him look devilish and sinister. The sudden gay, jaunty flash of his eyes was electric,

immortal. I told him once that he'd live to be a thousand. 'I shall,' he said.

When he had finished the digging and was scraping the light sun-dry soil from his spade with his flattened thumb I got up languidly from under the hedge.

'Don't strain yourself,' he said.

He shouldered his spade airily and walked away towards the house and I followed him, marvelling at his age, his strength, and his tirelessness under that hot sun. Half-way up the garden path he stopped to show me his gooseberries. They were as large as young green peaches. He gathered a handful, and the bough, relieved of the weight, swayed up swiftly from the earth. When I had taken a gooseberry he threw the rest into his mouth, crunching them like a horse eating fresh carrots. Something made me say, as I sucked the gooseberry:

'You must have been born about the same year as Hardy.'

'Hardy?' He cocked his bloodshot eye at me. 'What Hardy?'

'Thomas Hardy.'

He thought a moment, crunching gooseberries.

'I recollect him. Snotty little bit of a chap, red hair, always had a dew-drop on the end of his nose. One o' them Knotting Fox Hardies. Skinny lot. I recollect him.'

'No, not him. I mean another Hardy. Different man.'

'Then he was afore my time.'

'No, he was about your time. You must have heard of him. He wrote books.'

The word finished him: he turned and began to stride off towards the house. 'Books,' I heard him mutter, 'Books!' And suddenly he turned on me and curled his wet red lips and said in a voice of devastating scorn, his bloodshot eye half-angry, half-gleeful:

'I daresay.' And then in a flash: 'But could he grow goosegogs like that?'

Without pausing for an answer, he strode off again, and I followed him up the path and out of the blazing white afternoon sun into the cool, geranium-smelling house, and there he sat down in his shirt-sleeves in the big black-leathered chair that he once told me his

grandmother had left him, with a hundred pounds sewn in the seat that he sat on for ten years without knowing it.

'Mouthful o' wine?' he said to me softly, and then before I had time to answer he bawled into the silence of the house:

'Woman! If you're down the cellar bring us a bottle o' cowslip!'

'I'm upstairs,' came a voice.

'Then come down. And look slippy.'

'Fetch it yourself!'

'What's that, y'old tit? I'll fetch you something you won't forget in a month o' Sundays. D'ye hear?' There was a low muttering and rumbling over the ceiling. 'Fetch it yourself,' he muttered. 'Did ye hear that? Fetch it yourself!'

'I'll fetch it,' I said.

'You sit down,' he said. 'What do I pay a housekeeper for? Sit down. She'll bring it.'

I sat down in the broken-backed chair that in summer time always stood by the door, propping it open. The deep roof dropped a strong black shadow across the threshold but outside the sun blazed unbrokenly, with a still, intense mid-summer light. There was no sound or movement from anything except the bees, droll and drunken, as they crawled and tippled down the yellow and blue and dazzling white throats of the flowers.

THE LILY

85

WHEN YOU live absolutely in the centre of a country, as we did in Northamptonshire, the sight of the sea on a shining summer's day can only be likened to the sudden sight of the Promised Land.

THE VANISHED WORLD

THREE MORNINGS later Pop woke to see a clear limpid blue sky shining beyond the windows. Somebody, he could only suppose Ma, had already drawn back the curtains and now brilliant early sunlight was streaming strongly into the bedroom. Lying flat on his back, without pillows, he had a slightly upward view of the summer sky and against it, at the edge of the open window, a single rose-leaf, new, pink-copper in colour and slightly curled, not unlike a curved sea-shell half transparent in the sun.

He watched this single leaf for some long time. Soon he saw it not as a shell but a map, a small leaf-island crossed by a central river, with many little tributaries and a host of even tinier streams. At the edges of it the brightness of sun, clear gold, created an illusion of delicate little waves breaking on the leaf-shore; and the sky the further illusion that the sea itself was spread far beyond it, an expanse blue as chicory flower, and marvellously calm. This leaf-island and its surrounding summer sea he saw as something not merely wonderful; it was a miracle. It was yet another experience that illness incredibly magnifies the most trivial of things.

His long preoccupation with the marvel and loveliness of this single simple rose-leaf also created in him the strongest feeling of suspense. He might have been poised in space, a leaf himself, breathlessly held in air. He took several long, deep breaths: he felt unbearably glad to be alive.

A LITTLE OF WHAT YOU FANCY

THE STREAM came languidly down through flat meadows, turning with long shallow bends, flowing almost to stillness in dark pools lying without sunlight under arches of hawthorn and elder-trees, escaping again to narrow reaches of white stones and sand where the water flashed swiftly, without depth. The banks were steep and between the tufts of tall grass the earth was soft and reddish, like dark sand. Here and there willow-trees strained out over the water and in the moist places there were late forget-me-nots that had not lost their delicacy and forests of willow-herb flecked with pink bloom.

CHARLOTTE'S ROW

DURING THE rest of July Tom would wait about in the backyard of The Angel on Sunday afternoons, and soon after two o'clock Rosie would appear at the back door dressed all in white, from her white kid boots laced high up and her white dress full and flouncing in the skirt to her big leghorn hat and her white gloves skin-tight to her elbows, and Tom would hold her hand while she climbed down into the pub's best boat that Joe had moored in readiness against the jetty, Rosie steadying herself by pressing hard against the boat-bottom with the ferrule of her white sunshade. ''Bout settled?' Tom would say and when Rosie was ready he would push off, rowing strongly but with restraint, the oars splashing softly in the deserted silence of the Sunday afternoon, Rosie opened her sunshade as the boat drew away from the jetty and went upstream. Straw hat level, coat buttoned, Tom would row as though by mechanical impulses, in and out, in and out eternally, without variation of rhythm or pace, and after a while Rosie would lie back on the boat cushions, her body looking splendid and in some way stronger and finer under the pure white dress, to watch him until the everlasting backward and forward rhythm of his arms and body and the soft passage of the boat through the water almost sent her to sleep.

A HOUSE OF WOMEN

I REMEMBER a July afternoon in my Uncle Silas' garden when the raspberries were as big as walnuts and very nearly black. Where sun and shade met on the edge of the hazel spinney a line quivered all afternoon like pure white fire and far and deep under the trees the shade was black too.

We were supposed to be gathering raspberries for jam-making, but I was eating most of mine as I picked them and Silas wasn't working very hard either. He was lying flat on his back between the tall dark rows of canes with his head on his rolled-up jacket and a soft straw hat on his face. Now and then he lifted up the rim of the straw hat like a trap door and dropped a raspberry into his mouth, smacking his wet red lips with the sound of a clapper.

SHANDY LIL

IN THE warm July afternoon Primrose was dressed – if the word was not inappropriate – in an almost transparent yellow blouse with small red spots on it and the briefest of mini-skirts in delicate green. The blouse was remarkable for being less of a blouse than a piece of loose material tied across her breasts, revealing six or seven inches of bare midriff and navel below and an even wider expanse of naked flesh above. The mini-skirt contained hardly less material and from under it her legs swept in brown, ravishing curves. Ma guessed that she was wearing neither stockings nor tights and also rather suspected she was not wearing panties either. You could hardly blame her though, Ma told herself as she glanced at the rich curves of Primrose's firm high breasts protruding over the open blouse: the afternoon was hot enough for anything.

A LITTLE OF WHAT YOU FANCY

IN THE first week of August trees of early unnamed apples began to ripen in the garden at the back of the house, where no one had ever gathered them for years. 'We allus call 'em harvest pippins,' Tom said. 'Sour as hogs' wash.'

'Don't you never gather them?' the girl said.

'They allus come just at harvest and we never got time. Wheat's more consequence 'n apples.'

'Well, it may be. But all the same, I can't stand by and see good apples rot on the tree.'

In the first ten days of August she gathered forty bushels of apples. There was a warm odour of fruit in the house whenever he came in out of the hot sun. At the end of the ten days she made him drive in to

90

market. They loaded twenty sacks of apples into the trailer, and that afternoon, in the covered auction market, the apples made half a crown a bushel. 'Five pounds,' she said. 'Was it worth it?'

'Well,' he said. 'Well.'

'I'll do the same with the damsons and the walnuts and that tree of stewing pears.'

'If anybody 'd give me five pound I wouldn't ha' believed it.'

'Well, now you've got five pounds.'

'No,' he said. 'No. That I ain't. That's your own. You earned that.'

'You put it under the mattress,' she said. 'You'll need it soon enough.'

'No,' he said. 'No. It's yourn. You have it.'

'Put it under the mattress, I said.'

'You got to have some of it,' he said. 'Buy yourself something – buy yourself a present.'

'No, really,' she said.

'I want you to,' he said. 'I want to give you that.'

She smiled. 'All right. If it's not too much there is something I want. If it's not too much, I want a new dress.'

'It ain't too much,' he said. 'You go and get it while I have a look round.'

'No,' she said. 'If you're paying for it you're coming with me.'

He sat for nearly an hour on the upstairs floor of the dress-shop, watching her come out of the dressing cubicles wearing first one new dress and then another. He sat with his large hands on his knees, embarrassed because of the shop-girl, not knowing whether he liked the dresses because, for a long time, one seemed very like another. At last Edna came out of the cubicle wearing a light-blue silk that was smooth on her hips and breast. Her brown-gold arms and her face were lit up by the clean blue colour and he knew suddenly it was the one he wanted her to have.

'I'll just go and change it,' she said, 'and then choose a pair of stockings and we can go home.'

'Keep it on,' he said. 'Keep it on. I like to see it.'

'All right,' she said. 'Just till we get home.'

It was early evening when they drove back to the farm. Emmett was loading the milk-churns into the three-wheeler and the girl, seeing him, walked straight into the house, not speaking. Tom drove the car under the shed beyond the barn and then stopped to speak for a few moments with Emmett, who was sitting at the driving-wheel of the car. He told him how the apples had sold for five pounds, and after a few minutes Emmett drove away.

After Emmett had gone, Tom went into the house. The kitchen was empty. He called the girl, saying, 'Are you there?' He had never used her name. She did not answer and he went to the foot of the stairs and called again. There was no reply, and after a moment he went upstairs.

The door of her bedroom was open a little. He pushed it fully open with one hand and went in. As he saw her he stopped. She had taken off the new dress and was standing by the bed, in the evening sunlight, in her skirt. She smiled without speaking. He could see the brown edge of sunburn on her neck and shoulders and the deep hollow of her breasts that were cream above the edge of her pink skirt and below the brown rim of sun. He said something about wanting to see her in the new dress. She smiled again and let him put his hands on her bare warm shoulders. 'I've put it away,' she said. 'You'll just have to see me as I am.'

He stood for a moment looking down at her, sick and trembling. Her body, alight with the evening sun, was very warm, as if with reflected sun.

'I like you,' he said at last. 'God, I like you.'

'I like you,' she said. 'I always have. I shouldn't have come unless I did.'

'You're goin' to stop here?' he said. 'You ain't goin' now?'

'Going?' she said. 'What makes you think that? I'm not going.'

'I just wanted to know . . . I just wanted to be sure.'

She opened her arms and stretched them upward until they held him. He could feel the soft pressure of her firm, strong breasts against his body and the steady tenderness of the palms of her warm hands on his face.

'It's just as sure now as anything ever is.'

THE LITTLE FARM

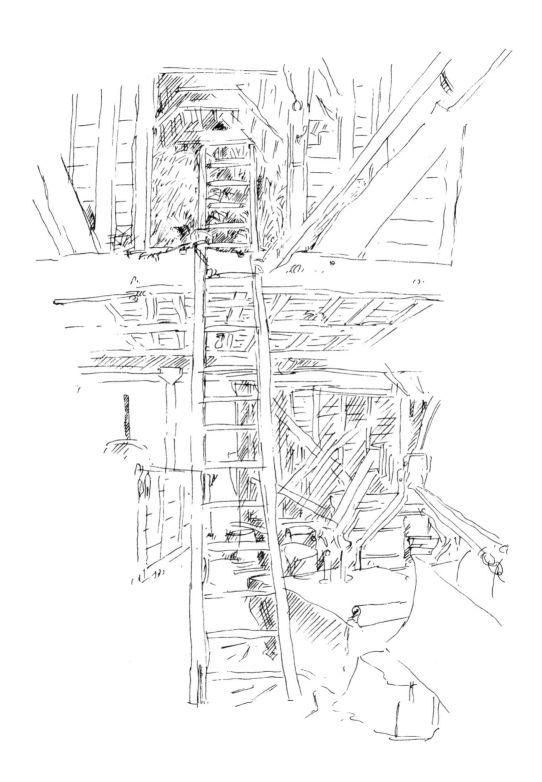

AUGUST BEGAN with mornings of thin soft cloud that cleared before noon into days that shimmered with heat, in silence, under blue-white skies. From the cottoned valley the white mist of summer drew off rapidly, leaving a river low and sluggish in scorched meadows, bright as opaque glass. All along the white central valley, so far from the sea, heat locked itself in, burning windlessly on cracked clay-lands, over brown-burnt beanfields and on acres of blistered wheat and whiter barley.

THE FEAST OF JULY

THE AUGUST rain is heavy and dark; it seems to blacken the green of the trees and wash out the burnished shine on the wheat. At the same time it gives the oats a fresh, airy grace. Beads of clear rain hang on the beards. The black seeds are shown up like darts. The oat-stalks are washed clean, opalescent, and all through the rainy, windless days they do not move. For some days the wheat has an astonishing colour, especially against the hedgerows. It is part green, part gold, partly the colour of dark honey. The colours shade into each other and are more than ever like waves as the wind gently blows the corn.

IN THE HEART OF THE COUNTRY

THERE FOLLOWED a miraculous summer: very hot, very dry, with long months of drought. In its scintillating brilliance I retraced with great happiness some of the steps of childhood, some of them leading to a little earthly paradise consisting merely of three narrow meadows flanked by a stream where often and often as a boy I had gathered watercress with my grandfather. I suppose they were perhaps really very ordinary, those meadows and that stream, but to me they were then, and still remain today, like the distilled essence of paradise. Here and there the stream ran shallow over white and sepia stones; in a few places it deepened into black holes shadowed by ancient bushes of sloe. In spring silver and yellow sallows positively seemed to dance with bees. Little fish darted, silver and gold too, in and out of shadow and sunlight. In August forests of pink willow-herb, of the sort known as codlins-and-cream, softly filled long stretches of the banks, together with purple loosestrife and tall cane-like reeds, feathery brown at the tips. On hot days cows sought shade under vast old hawthorns, rubbing their backs against them until the trunks shone like polished mahogany. The air, bereft of bird song, whirred with that concentrated chorus of grasshoppers that seems in the strangest way to deepen silence, so that the air was hotly and hauntingly hushed. Even the yellowhammers, on those intensely hot days of late summer, were silent, as if thirstily asleep, and on many an afternoon I lay, sweating in some pool of dark parched tree-shadow, and slept too. And thus I would find myself healed again.

THE BLOSSOMING WORLD

THAT YEAR, the hottest for ten years, it was a better harvest than they had hoped. Corn ripened swiftly. Barley was white before the rustle of oat-heads had quietened in the rick-yard, beans were scorched from sun-split pods like coffee-berries, the crop spilling under the hook. Luck was with them: day after day followed each other without rain like the clear pages of a book, the heat white as paper. They worked on into moonlight, the peace of ghostly August stubbles shattered by the tractor, made more ghostly by the clack of cartwheels and the rustle of feet and forks on the sun-scorched straw.

A HOUSE OF WOMEN

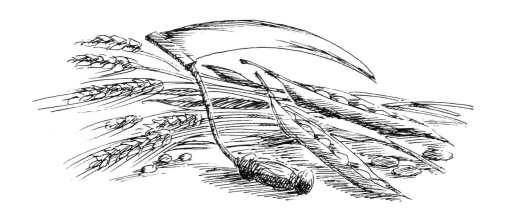

HARVEST BROUGHT them together again. Every autumn Bishop would negotiate for the work of harvesting from a neighbouring farmer, and towards the middle of August the whole family would go out to the fields, living and working there until the last shock had been carried, the women returning again for the gleaning. In early August, when the corn was in full ear but not yet ripened, Bishop would call at the farmhouse standing beyond the great walnut tree under which the Bishops had once lived. He would ask for Spong, the farmer, and together they would walk through the stack-yard and down the meadow-lane and into the ripening fields of corn. Like a man in a daydream Bishop would stare across the soft running waves made by the light wind on the delicate white oats or at the heavy wheat ears just beginning to drop with their own weight in the blaze of sunshine. And finally he would run his hands softly among the cornstalks and say:

'What are ye going to give us?'

And Spong would look away over the field too and say that he would give this or that price for reaping and tying, by the field or the acre, with harvest beer thrown in. The price would vary from year to year, with the lightness and fullness of the crop, and after looking away again over the field Bishop would say, 'It's a tidy yield, master,' and Spong would consider it and gaze across the field again and then put a fraction on the price. Then Bishop would consider it and then spit and say, 'The beer ain't good enough,' and after a moment or two in a pretence of thought Spong would name another quart a day. Bishop, satisfied, would gaze for the last time across the ripening field and remark, 'Looks to me oughter be ready about th' eleventh.' Surprised, Spong would say, 'I reckoned not till th' eighteenth, Bish,' but Bishop would shake his head. 'I'll be along about th' eleventh, any road,' he would say, and the deal would be over.

The harvest that year was early and by the middle of August the oats were down. The Bishops would be in the field soon after daybreak, Mrs Bishop bringing the day's food in a shoemaker's truck, wheeling the truck under the hedge on the north side of the field. They began work at once in the morning coolness, Bishop and Luke mowing, the women gathering and binding, the girls making the bonds and their mother binding the sheaves. Except for the noon rest and the mid-morning breakfast and the pauses for drinking the work went on all day, until darkness came. Bishop mowed throughout the day with serene strength, as though tireless, his changeless motions having no effort in them. With the scythe in his hands he was a new man, nothing of the shoemaker or the poacher left about him except his black bowler, which he wore all day as though he had forgotten it. At fixed intervals he stopped to drink; all day a soft beer-coloured sweat stood on his sun-brown arms and face. He mowed in silence: but it was a new silence, an expression of his satisfaction in the sound of his scythe among the harsh cornstalks and in the sight of his swathe lying yellow and beautiful on the stubble behind him.

THE POACHER

OUR DINNER in the harvest-field was always hot; none of your make-shift lumps of dough with onions stuffed into them: a dish known as a Bedfordshire Clanger; no lumps of cold bacon and bread, no plain bread-and-cheese, no sandwiches. In one basket would repose a steak-and-kidney pie, perhaps a rabbit pie, or a beef pudding, together with basins of new potatoes, carrots, peas or beans: all wrapped in clean white napkins. In the other there would be, perhaps, an apple pie or, what I myself loved best of all, a pie of a small yellow local plum of extraordinarily good flavour and rather squarish in shape and touched with a faint blush of crimson, very like an apricot.

To eat all this we sat, on very hot days, in the shade of a vast ash-tree, or if the weather were a little cooler, in the shelter of a wheat stook. All about us the deep summer silence spread in a vast hush broken only, though really accentuated, by the whirr of grasshoppers and occasion-ally, from down the hedgerows, the crooning song of yellowham-mers, deepening the silence too with their endless 'little bit of bread-and-cheese'. 'Pass the pepper and salt, boy,' my grandfather would say and eventually, replete, would fall into a doze, at which signal I crept away along the hedgerow to look for the first dewberries, the sweet-sharp taste of which still bursts on my tongue as the true juice of full summer.

THE VANISHED WORLD

ALONE, ON a day in August, she walked across the marsh, along the dykes. A keen wind, quite cold, was blowing in from the sea, ruffling and bending brown feathered reeds, pale lilac heads of marsh-mallow, purple torches of loose-strife. The many grazing sheep on the pastures were accompanied by white-grey flocks of gulls, feeding and spasmodically flying from one field to another. The towers of the power station, some distance down the coast, had the appearance of some curious castle, ancient but new, the colour of grey sand.

It was her intention to walk the four miles or so to the sea. She would, she felt, feel freer by the sea. A solitary imprisonment on the marsh, alone in the cottage, an entire month of the simple life, had become tolerable no longer. She had to walk, see the sea, acquaint herself with a new horizon.

Winter, as she had always felt it did, had once again begun in August. The voices of sea-gulls were harsh on the wind. There was a cold, clenching touch of salt in the air and ahead of her a heron rose from the dykes in slow flight, a grey ghost watching for prey.

THE SIMPLE LIFE

THE BUS stopped on the corner below the hill. She had to walk the last mile to the farm. In two or three days it would be September. A few late fingers of honeysuckle, pale yellow, touched with flecks of strawberry, were still flowering on the high bank above the lane and she suddenly felt an impulse to climb the bank to gather them.

From there she could see across a copse of hazel that had been cut down in springtime. Beyond it great beeches, still green, faintly brown only when scorched by sun, rose for almost a mile along the steep hillside of chalk. And as she stood there, gathering the honeysuckle, smelling it, thinking a little, she saw the young keeper walking down the path.

He saw her at the same moment and began to come down beside the hazel copse, almost as if he had been waiting for her. She saw him coming and began to behave at once as if she had not seen him, going on gathering the honeysuckle, turning her back, slowly walking away down the hill.

'I got something I wanted to say,' he said.

'Oh?'

Slowly she picked off sprigs of honeysuckle, not looking at him.

'I been wanting to see you,' he said.

DULCIMA

102

ON A day in late summer all the beauty of summer rises like cream to the hills. The clouds come riding in from the sea. They are very white, but the waves of shadow unfolding across the white stubbles move with dark splendour, and in the wide blue intervals the sun is very hot under the wall of beeches. All across the open slope of downland the late flowers are in their glory. Where the beeches end there begins a narrow thicket of dogwood and wild clematis and spindle and black-berry, and where the thicket ends there begins a steep run of pink and mauve and yellow that ends only far down the slope, at the edge of the summer-bleached arable land. The wild clematis is in flower in lacy cream wreaths everywhere; the spindle-berries are already touched with rose; the dewberries are black and luscious as they trail on the ground where the last small wild strawberries glow very scarlet among the flowers. There are a few wild raspberries and in one place, looking like strings of red bryony, a tree of wild red currant, dark scarlet, shining, untouched by birds. Soon there will be nothing but a glow of berry and leaf and seed all along the down; but now, in late summer, not quite autumn, all the glory is in the flowers, and on hot afternoons, when even the wind is warm, in the drowsy crowds of butterflies that float everywhere like wind-shaken petals of scarlet and white and blue and coffee-brown.

IN THE HEART OF THE COUNTRY

THE SUMMER of 1921 was incredibly long and hot. No rain fell for several months. A summer virtually beginning in February lasted on until November. Great cracks, almost chasms, broke up the clay of harvest-fields. Beans shot from their grilled black stalks like bullets. There were many fires. My grandfather and his fellow firemen, already considerably frustrated by a pair of greys who, somehow sensing fire, always either reared up on their hind-legs or reverted to the disposition of donkeys at the mere sound of the alarm, were further hampered by the fact that the greys sometimes also lay down and then took a good half hour to harness, so that very often the fire was out before the scorching chariot arrived. More often than usual that summer we heard the fire-bell clanking up the road. Instantly scythe and rake and pitch-fork would be dropped as we rushed to harness the horse, just in time to follow the chariot and its fuming greys, now at full pelt, as they passed the farm-gate, the firemen hanging on to the engine and shouting with the enthusiasm of small boys going to a bun-fight. Somehow I was always just in time to hang on to the backboard of the truck, eventually to arrive on a scene where the only source of water, a brook, had long since dried up in the drought, and a row of thatched cottages or a couple of haystacks smouldered like black funeral pyres in the intense heat of afternoon.

THE VANISHED WORLD

AUGUST BURNED into September until the shorn lobes of grassland were the colour of the fox we were always stalking but could not catch and the only green was in the great sprays of hawthorn and the water-weeds about the brook. When the barley was finished we carried it and stacked it in the yard. It was our only crop, and the land on which it had grown was fissured like the cracked dry basin of a pond, still too hard for ploughing.

LOVE FOR LYDIA

105

AUTUMN

SEPTEMBER COMES in with dark-blue gales and early mornings savage
with thunder rain, with days clogged and humid as a bakehouse, the
pall of cloud dark as January.

THE COUNTRY OF WHITE CLOVER

THE SECOND time I went to dinner it was already September. The mild
misty evenings were drawing in. The weather was soft and humid.
There were mushrooms in the meadows. I mention this because,
earlier that evening, we actually went down to the fields and gathered
mushrooms which were afterwards served on toast, as a savoury. After
that we ate pears for dessert, the lovely Marie Louise variety, peeling
the smooth red skin with little pearl-handled silver knives.

'September is a good month for moths,' he said. 'Would you like to
go out after dinner and see what we can find?'

So presently we were walking with a torch through the mullein
wilderness, past the choked raspberry canes. He stood quite still once
or twice, steadily shining the torch into the darkness under fruit
boughs. A desultory moth or two began to dance in the light and he
said:

'I didn't bring the cyanide bottle. It's hardly worth it. Mostly what
you can see are common *Noctuae*.'

Soon I thought he seemed nervous. He kept switching on the torch
and then suddenly putting it off again. One moment the air was
dancing with a crowd of small light wings and the next I was groping,
half-blinded, for the path among the grasses.

Suddenly he put out the light for the sixth or seventh time, stopped
abruptly and took me by the shoulders.

'I want to ask you to marry me,' he said. His hands were shaking dreadfully. 'Will you? I know there is a great difference – but would you? Would you consider it please?'

I simply wanted to laugh outright at him.

'Now I see,' I told him, 'what moth it was you hoped to find out here. The rare nocturnal Laura, eh?'

Nervously he started panting, breathing hard.

'No,' he said. 'No. It's simply – well, I've been trying to say this for some time. Would you? – would you marry me?'

'It's very sweet of you, but – '

'Would you think it over? Think it over and give me an answer another day?'

It was quite ludicrous; he was breathing hard on me, as if blowing on a hot potato.

'Oh! no, really,' I started to say. 'Thank you, but – ' After all what sort of encouragement had I given him to get him to the point of asking me this?

'You've kissed me very often. You've given me such a lot of pleasure,' he said. 'It's been six weeks since you kissed me that Sunday afternoon – '

'Yes, but kissing,' I said. 'Kissing is kissing and there's a great deal of difference between kissing and getting married. You're old enough to know that.'

THE QUEEN OF SPAIN FRITILLARY

109

By the time plums had grown purple-fat on trees and had been gathered, the real festival of the year, the English *vendange*, the hop-picking, began, bringing the centuries-old fusion of Cockneys from London and the people of Kent, in almost precisely the way peasants forgather for grape-harvests in autumn in European vineyards.

I always felt that this festival, for which surely every working family turned out, was not only gay, as indeed it was with all the chaff and joking old-buck backchat and teasing and beery fighting and wenching that went on in and around it, was something more than just the mere business of picking hops for brewers; it always struck me as being a sort of pagan rite. And thus, I always felt, the people of Kent perhaps also saw it, though not of course consciously; it was a rite that had to be attended, a festival that had to be worshipped at. Nobody, except toffs and squires, ever missed hop-picking. Every mother took every child with her to the hop-gardens and every child, except those still being suckled at the breast, picked hops, from the first dewy misty light of September mornings until the soft descent of dusk and its shouted evening benediction that rang out down the pale green lines of fallen or half-fallen hop-skeins: 'Pull no more bine!'

THE BLOSSOMING WORLD

110

THE AFTERNOON sunshine fell softly on the backs of the women advancing along the hillside in a ragged line, on their bowed heads, as on the stone spire and the brown roofs obtruding from the plain below, as on the burnt hillside, the empty cornfields and the red, golden and dark leaves of the woods it lay with the quiet magic benediction of autumn.

Everywhere hung a great stillness as if a blessing were being bestowed upon those things: only the women, as if oblivious, moved beneath it, unevenly, stooping, rising and going on.

Each of the women had a sack with her. Sometimes a faint breeze played among their skirts and sent a ripple through the crooked line. Haunting the edge of the woodside, thrusting themselves into the hedges, straddling the ditches, loosening stumps of rotted wood with their feet, all the time the sound of their voices filled the clear, hushed air of the afternoon like the chatter of strange birds.

THE FUEL-GATHERERS

By the middle of September they had become passionately devoted. When she went to see him in a wild storm of rain and leaves or under some benign blue sky, the storm excited her and the sunshine and the long slender shadows of afternoon filled her with an eager, sensual warmth. At home, where pears had already begun to drop heavily in frosty nights from among copper leaves, she thought unceasingly of him. By turns her love lay heavily, joyously or lightly upon her. The big round berries of an Indian rose turned deep orange, a bush of marjoram withered from frost. An apple branch split off in a storm, and now sometimes the garden looked desolate after rain. But by afternoon the sun created soft magic illusions, as if spring had come, and she had long, tender, illusory moods when she dreamed and in fancy gave herself to him.

CATHERINE FOSTER

THE COUNTRYSIDE was wonderfully green, a wet autumn having kept the leaves green and late on the trees and honeysuckle was still blooming on the hedgerows and sweet-peas were still a tangle of pink and cream and blue among the hazel sticks in the garden. The land lay quiet and lovely, the stubble silvery-yellow and the ploughed land warm and red in the soft sunlight.

THE FALLOW LAND

THE THIN tongue of coast was so flat that it was like a scar on the sea. Nothing rose above the level of the one-storeyed shacks scattered about it like cubes of sea-worn wreckage except a lighthouse, standing up like a vast white candle in a wide lofty sky, so that from a distance it seemed to float in air.

By the end of September, after the heat of summer, the sea-flowers were dead. A long flat tide floated in, almost limped in, washing over and over again the same wide salt-grey waste of sand, the same bright fringe of shingle, black with fresh-strewn seaweed and sprinkled with pretty white and rose and turquoise shells. Salt dust blew on small winds from one side of the road to the other, rattling harshly on steely patches of sea-thistle and dune-grass, and then blew back again. It drifted finely against the shacks, with their sun-spent flowers, that would soon be closed for winter, and buried the steps of their porches a little deeper every day.

THE LIGHTHOUSE

THE WEATHER was very beautiful that autumn when we first began dancing. The valley seemed always to be dreamy with light mists, sometimes a smoke-straw colour, sometimes pale amber-rose, that broke into October days of tender fly-drowsy sunshine. We used to go to the dances in an old black Chrysler limousine with a glass division and occasional seats at the back that I hired, in the first place and almost by chance, from Johnson's garage down beyond the station.

LOVE FOR LYDIA

SEVERAL WEEKS later, about five o'clock on a warm October evening, Pop, in his shirt sleeves, was sitting comfortably in a deck chair on the south side of the house, a quart glass of beer at his side, occasionally potting with a shot gun at odd pheasants flying over from the Jerebohm domain to roost in the bluebell wood beyond the yard.

It was just the sort of shooting the doctor ordered. You sat in comfort, with a nice supply of beer at hand, and picked off the birds like one o'clock. Perfick sport. Like fishing for trout with worms, he didn't suppose it was the real and proper sporting thing to do, but at the same time he reckoned it was streets in front of tramping over sodden stubbles on rainy winter afternoons, waiting for birds to be beaten out of copses at ten quid a time. The pheasant tasted no different anyway and he was very glad he'd managed to persuade Mr Jerebohm to buy a couple of hundred young ones at precisely the right time. Well fed on

corn, the birds had fattened beautifully in the extraordinary warm autumn weather and were now as tender and tasty, he thought, as young love. Now and then you missed a bird because at the critical moment you had the beer up to your lips, but on the whole he couldn't grumble. He'd bagged a brace already.

WHEN THE GREEN WOODS LAUGH

BY THE middle of October most of the leaves of the chestnuts in the square had fallen, curled like brandy-snaps, dry and shrivelled, to be followed presently by softer yellower shoals from limes in streets leading out of the square. In the orchard the pear leaves turned a peculiar fine bright crimson, hanging on still days like breathless fire, and then suddenly flickering and pattering down in quick turns of autumn wind.

THE SLEEPLESS MOON

PRESENTLY THE first few sharp snaps of October frost coloured horn-beams and maples a pure daffodil gold and soon sweet chestnut leaves were swimming down through the still air like slow shoals of brown-yellow fish, slapping against baring branches as they fell.

THE MAN WHO LOVED SQUIRRELS

SHE WAS burning chaff in three big yellow separate heaps as he came across the field. A flame was darting up and along the blue-black edge of each heap like lamp-wick, leaving smoking ash behind.

She stood leaning on the long white handle of a hay-fork, arms firm and crooked, hands just below her chin, eyes rather low on the three smoking heaps, as if she was not really watching him at all. The wind was cold for October. It blew in sudden ugly gusts, switching smoke over grey-yellow stubble in blue flat clouds that turned back and bit each other like dogs at play.

CHAFF IN THE WIND

SUMMER AND autumn fuse into each other imperceptibly, the point of fusion lost in some period of September humidity, in a mild wonder of too-soft days. Autumn comes slowly, and having come slowly, goes on slowly, for a long time, even as far on as December. In a country of many trees, such as this is, where one kind of tree turns its colours while another holds them fast and where some trees are stripped while others are summered with leaf, it is never easy to make the mark between season and season. Autumn slips a finger into August, but Spring has a revenge in December. Winter blows on September, but October still remains, with May and June, the loveliest month of the English year, a kind of second spring, uncertain but exhilarating, sunny and snowy, hot and frosty, bright and dark by turns, a sort of autumnal April.

With it, the woods are at their best again. On some day in late October, after a night of frost, the sweet-chestnuts come showering down like prickled apples, splitting against the boughs as they fall, opening to cream-coloured cups in which the chestnuts lie tight-sandwiched, like fat mahogany peardrops. But generally, so early, there is no breaking of the cup and the nut-case lies almost as inviolable on the ground as on the tree, a fierce ball of pricks needing courage and strength to break. The gathering of these nuts is a great business in the south. The woods become places of pilgrimage, not so much for the country folk, who have an astonishing disregard for the fruits of the earth lying at their back doors, as for the townsfolk. Out they come, by bus and car and bike, principally men, very earnest, and principally on Sunday mornings. It is a piece of yearly ritual. They raid the woods like human squirrels, spending hours kneeling or stooping or even sitting under the canopy of leaves already much thinned by rain and frost, foraging among the blanket of fallen leaf and husk, filling cans and sacks with the silk-soft nuts, staggering out at last under the weight of their pot-bellied sacks, still looking very earnest but, somehow, satisfied.

And since it is a kind of common ritual, off we go too: infants and pram and basket and bags and the lot. We also like the nuts, though not ravenously. Still, it does not matter. Once in the wood, we are like the rest. We kneel and sit and stoop under the great trees and split open the fat emerald shells and gather the mahogany harvest. There is a great smell of autumn everywhere: great in the literal sense, an all-pervading, powerful odour, universal and bountiful, that changeless autumn formula of warmth and wet, of drip and decay. In the heart of the wood it is thick and drowsy, almost a fermentation. It drowses and drunkens everything.

The two infants are small and feminine. They wear pantaloons of blue or pink silk, about as large as decent paper bags, that are just not adequate enough to cover their pink bottoms. They stagger and stumble on small legs and flop and half-drown in the thick sea of fallen leaves and husks. They are both fair, with hair four or five shades lighter than primroses. But on the one it is straight as grass and on the other it curls like a thousand silky sweet-pea tendrils. I foresee for them a future of distinguished devilry. With the faces of angels, they have the world weighed up. They are beyond all hoodwinking or cheating or delusion. It's all a game, and their parents, like the spanish chestnuts, are just part of it.

And down there, in the wood one day, tired of gathering chestnuts, they roamed and gathered something else: many umbrellas of fungus. It was my first revelation of the range and brilliance of English fungi. That afternoon we gathered them of all sizes from the size of a pearl-button to a football, in all colours from white to black, from cream to purple, from yellow to scarlet. They grew everywhere, under leaves and on dead wood and living, lifting up pads of decayed leaf and earth, forcing their way past fallen trunks and up through tangles of briar and living leaf. They filled the wood with their sombre rotten-sweet odour of decay. We gathered boleti that were like sponge-cakes: greenish olive yellow underneath, or faint rose, or creamy white. The infants returned triumphant with scarcely visible infantile parasols of old-maidish dingy mauve or brown. We found many little clavaria of mauve and pink and white, like sea-coral, small branching stems of almost untouchable delicacy. And everywhere silk-gilled parasols of sepia and cream and pigeon-grey and stone-colour; and suddenly some rarer, quite dazzling specimens in orange or scarlet or crimson or purple, big and gaudy; and rarer still some yellow-bellied thing, something of slimy lizardish green or a strange, too-pure sinister white. And all under the birches, large and small, tight and flaunting, that too-handsome *Amarita muscaria*, like a Russian cake in looks and somehow like a Russian villainess by name, poisonously scarlet, and decorated, like some precious cake, with its rich flecks of almond. This Amarita, the fly-agaric, is said to be eaten in Russia, though extremely poisonous. But then the Russians, to whom fungi are like a creed, will eat anything. In Russia, too, Amarita is said to be used, like hashish in the East, as a means of drugged intoxication. Gathered and dried, it has some powerful narcotic effect. Moreover, one fungus goes a long way, since the power of it will continue, with a tiny extra daily flip, for a week. There is generally much needless panic, among country folk especially, regarding fungus. But Amarita justifies it. Under the quiet birches, on the soft rain-mild October days, she is somehow too brilliant. She looks sinister, and that lovely dome-shaped cake, poppy-scarlet, is deadly.

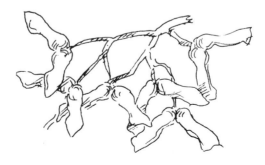

With fungus and nuts and the spinning seeds of sycamore, the autumn reaches its heart. We talk of the height of summer, the dead of winter, the fullness of spring. But autumn reaches a heart, a core of fruitfulness and decline, that has in it the sweet dregs of the year. Under the quiet skies the woods stand now with a kind of contradictory magnificence: gaudy and smouldering, flaring and almost arrogant, the stain of yellow and bronze spreading and deepening among the green, the copper flames of beeches firing whole sections of the woods with stationary heatless fires that look perpetual. Even the green now is burning. It has the yellow of flame in it. It bears some faint relation to the green flames of fires on nights of frost. And when frost comes now, it is paradoxically not to extinguish or lessen these vast flames of leaf, but to sting them into a finer richness and fierceness. The wood in the lane, more birch and oak than anything, smoulders only in a continual cloud of yellow. It is the woods on the hills, with their great structures of beech and larch, that make the vast day-fires of copper and orange and even, sometimes, crimson, all flame except for the plaything tufts of wild clematis seed tangled on the outer edges of the wood, little sheep-wool tufts of still smoke that even the rage of winter never quite blows away.

And now there is also a kind of second spring of flowers. In the woods it is honeysuckle mostly, cool and now almost white-fingered and unseen as it hangs among young chestnut and hazel. On the woodsides it is the final flush of willow-herb, the last creaming of meadowsweet in the ditches, the last petticoat-pink rags of campion. By the water-side willow herb also goes on, and meadow-sweet, and a few solitary magenta brushes of loosestrife. There is no flush of bloom. Wherever it is, it is accidental, modest, an aftermath. It is symbolic in every way of autumn, which is not so much a season of itself as a remembrance and a foretaste of seasons. The year distils itself into October. Rain and sun and frost and wind and death act like balm, so that there is a miraculous clarifying and softening of everything, until the limpid days are like wine.

THROUGH THE WOODS

Soon it would be November. There would be that touch of frost white like thick dew on morning grasses. The oaks would turn their gold-tan colour, with their deep tan-smell of decay. The late afternoons when he came in from hunting would be blue – not exactly blue, not quite grey, but a mysterious half-colour of great softness. The days at the end of November, as they nearly always did, would grow completely tranquil and without wind and the sound of hounds crying over great distances would be the first sharp herald of winter-time.

THE SLEEPLESS MOON

One afternoon in late October she walked through the beech-wood, above the farm, to the keepers' hut on the far slope of the hill. The leaves of the beeches were already making masses of fire against a sky that was blue and lofty and under them the glow of air was a pure orange, full of dancing flies.

The door of the keepers' hut was open but the hut was empty and her feeling of disappointment was so sharp that it took her by surprise. She had not expected that. Inside the hut there was a table, a camp-bed, two chairs, an oil-stove and a few cups and a box below the bed. A row of oiled steel traps hung on one wall and a neat pile of newspapers lay on the table, with a pair of leather gloves and a canvas bag.

She felt a curious uneasy sensation of excitement as she looked at these things. There was a neatness, a swept homeliness about the hut that fascinated her. A bucket with a galvanized lip for soap stood in one corner with a towel folded over the side. A mirror by the window

122

above it had a hairbrush and comb hanging on one side and a razor-strop on the other.

For winter there was a stove and for some reason she thought suddenly of winter rain, of days of flying beech-leaves, of the little hut with the stove humming away behind the closed door. There was something wonderfully secure in thinking about these things, and that too took her by surprise.

She walked away up the hill. At the crest of it a breeze came over the bare western slope where the copses of hazel had been cut down. It blew her hair about her face and down over her cheeks in untidy strands. The honeysuckle the young man had spoken about had dropped its flowers and now hung with reddening berries over bushes of hawthorn.

DULCIMA

OFTEN BY early November a spell of thin searing wind began to whip in from the eastern coast, skimming down the hill like an icy water-fall. While the valley below still lay green there sometimes appeared long white tongues of snow on the upper hillside. The wind sang in crackling tones through the ramparts of beeches, still not stripped of final leaves, and along the fringes of woodland the big dark yews stood out blacker than ever.

On a morning just like this she went across the snow-flaked yard to the cow-shed, milk bucket in hand, a little later than usual. The air was so vicious with driving wind that she told herself it was too cold to snow any more. Barton was erecting hurdles for sheltering sheep on the lee-side of the yard, packing inside them a wall of straw.

THE TRIPLE ECHO

FOR TWO week-ends he did not jump at all. At the third he heard a clatter of pony hooves on the stable yard, looked up to see her long legs astride the pony and heard her deep voice say:

'I thought you must be ill, Mr Barnfield, because you weren't jumping. Mother sent me to inquire.'

Her voice, deeper than ever, he thought, startled and disturbed him; and he fumbled for words.

'Oh! no, oh! no. Perfectly all right, thank you. Oh! no. It's just that the countryside has been looking so lovely that I've been giving the jumps a miss and riding up on the hill instead. In fact I'm just going up there now.'

'Do you mind if I ride that way with you?' she said.

Some minutes later they were riding together up the hillside, under clumps of pines, along paths by which huge bracken fronds were already tipped with fox-brown. Late blackberries shone pulpy and dark with bloom in the morning sunlight and where the bracken cleared there ran rose-bright stains of heather, with snow-tufts of cotton-grass in seed.

'You can smell that wonderful, wonderful scent of pines,' she said.

DEATH OF A HUNTSMAN

EARLIER IN the afternoon they walked by the little lake. As late as the first week in November the lamps of the quinces hung miraculously suspended from the grey central islands of boughs and then gradually, one by one, dropped into the frosted reeds below.

By the middle of November there remained, on the south side of the island, where the sun caught it full in the early afternoons, one quince, the last of the autumn lanterns, and as Harry Barnfield and the girl came down the path through thinning alder trees she got into the way of running on ahead of him to the edge of the lake, always giving the same little cry:

'Look, Harry, our quince is still there!'

For about a week longer they watched, as if it were some marvellously suspended planet glowing above the wintry stretches of water where thin ice sometimes lingered white all day in the thickest shadow of reeds, the last remaining quince, suspended bare and yellow on frost-stripped boughs.

'When it falls I shall feel the summer has gone completely,' the girl said.

Soon Harry Barnfield felt as she did: that this was the last of summer poured into a single phial of honey. When it fell and split at last he knew he would hear, dark and snapping, the breath of winter.

By the fifteenth day of the month the quince, looking bigger and more golden than ever in an afternoon of pure, almost shrill blue sky already touched on the horizon by the coppery threat of frost, still remained.

'Look, Harry!' the girl said, 'our quince is still there!'

For some time they walked slowly by the lake. In the breathless blue afternoon the one remaining globe of fruit glowed more than ever like the distillation of all the summer.

DEATH OF A HUNTSMAN

WINTER

WINTER BEGAN with brusque wet storms from the west, that were followed by dry winds from the north-east, the direction of the sea, and from which the valley had no protection. Over the bare easterly shoulder of land the wind had a way of skimming and pouring like invisible ice, pitching down to river-level and then whipping up again to the westward hill, where the town lay raw and exposed, full in the lash of it.

THE FEAST OF JULY

ACROSS THE garden, from the terrace along which a few pale violet winter irises were in bloom, delicate as orchids in the December sun, I could see beyond an expanse of marshland the bright gold saucer of sun. Over the windless bay a track of low sunlight made an elongated pool of light exactly the colour of the sherry that clung to two or three glasses on a silver tray.

THE SUN OF DECEMBER

OUTSIDE THE air was cold, with a sense of snow. He walked quickly as he went through the town, skirting behind the Square, and out towards the bare flat country. As he walked across the wintry fields the wind came straight from the east into his face. He could see the clouds extending into the farthest distance like a series of shaggy waves, infinitely grey and sombre. He felt a sense of relief and pleasure as he walked and looked at the familiar country, deserted except for the sheep lying quiet under the hedges in the treeless fields and the flocks of peewits feeding on the dark ploughed land.

As he reached the higher country above Tichmarsh, under the shelter of the great belt of woods, the wind seemed to quieten down. He climbed the slope and looked back: the village with its square-towered church, the little white pub, the quiet bare fields beyond were all as familiar to him as his own hands. And for the first time in his life it gave him a conscious pleasure simply to stand there and look at it all.

It began to snow a little as he went on and down through the woods on the other side of the hill. The soft vague flakes seemed to be falling from the shaken branches of the trees. He hardly noticed them. Under the trees, out of the wind, there was a curious winter stillness over everything, the birds hushed, the rabbits rustling the dead leaves quietly.

THE POACHER

SNOW BEGAN to fall a day later as she came to a higher stretch of pasture country where the fields were no longer divided by water dykes but by walls of stone. There were many sheep in the fields in that part of the country and as the wind sharpened, turning north westward, spitting at first little frozen bullets of snow, she saw them huddling closer and closer under the lee of the walls, stone and wool the same grey-yellow colour against the pure fresh snow.

THE FEAST OF JULY

SUDDENLY, IN early December, the land seems strangely quiet and still. There is a sultriness as soft as milk over everything. There are brief spells of damp, windless weather, after rain, when whole days seem like soundless preludes to spring. The grass in pastures is thick and rich with an almost spring greenness and the trees stand out with new delicacy and colour against the half dark sky: fresh skeletoned shapes of black and red and grey and softest brown, the willows and osiers varnished a deep walnut, the trunks of sycamore and chestnut stained over with a silvery green fungus which clings to them like bright damp pollen, the smooth bark of the dog-wood as warm as claret against the harsh twigs of blackthorn. The branches of the trees are as still as death. The air is soft and mild and the distance half-obscured with lingering mist, so that the colours of the bare woods are dissolved into one colour, the tender blue of still smoke or shadows on snow.

THROUGH THE WOODS

THE SQUARE, deserted, all white under its street lamps, had the appearance of a small hushed desert in which the market cross made a pyramid in the centre. There was no longer any wind. Snow was still falling in large dreamy flakes. Already it hung thick, like big blown flowers, on the branches of the chestnut trees. From time to time one of these too heavy flowers of snow fell without a sound, an enormous bursting flake exploding under the street lights. And as she saw it she remembered the flake or two of snow that had fallen sharp and cold on her bare face in the moment before she had let herself be kissed by Frankie Johnson. It seemed a great while ago, that moment, but its expansion into full experience was still not complete. It was still much more like one deep and prolonged hush of suspense than an incident. Like the big flowers of snow hanging on the chestnut boughs, strained to breaking point until they fell and exploded, she felt herself still waiting for this single moment to break into fragments and take her with its fall.

THE SLEEPLESS MOON

FOR THE third year in succession winter fell on the same day. The long, wild, rainy autumn, the days of flying brown leaves herded by warm, wet sea-winds, broke at last on the Saturday before Christmas. The wind swung north, by afternoon it was very cold, by Sunday bitterly cold. By Monday the ponds were covered with ice that would bear, and by Tuesday there was snow. In 1939 it was snow such as no one had seen in England, so continuously at least and for so long, for fifty years and in many places for a hundred years.

That year there were many berries on the holly; in spring the trees everywhere had been covered by clusters of green-white, pink-touched blossom. There had been many berries, too, on the hawthorns, and there was a tree that stood claret-covered until the last week of December. The cold did not begin reluctantly, as it often does in England, but suddenly and bitterly and fiercely. It bit down on the earth like teeth. It bit with a black and scarring effect, so that the earth seemed skinned raw by wind and frost and the trees were bared down to the black bone of the branches. Then it began to snow with that mournful, silent beauty, steadily and relentlessly, that only a great storm of snow can give. There are sometimes wild and brief snows which merely pepper the ploughed land into bars of whiteness and shadow. But this snow covered everything. It came down without a break for a whole day, then for another day, and then for still another. For seventy-two hours, day and night, it drove down on a bitter wind from a sky that seemed solid with dirty grey clouds as far as heaven itself. Almost always after great snow the sky clears. It becomes cloudless, more blue than summer, sun and snow dazzling as light from a flashed mirror. But now the sky showed no sign of clearing. The clouds remained thick and sombre, dirty as a vast sheepskin. For a day there was intense frost, then a thaw, then frost again, but the sky did not change. It remained always that sombre and dirty grey, as if it had in it a vast world of unfallen snow.

IN THE HEART OF THE COUNTRY

A SPELL of fine, humid weather worked a miracle across the hills. Once more they became softened, tender and green. The frigid snowy air that had created such a sense of imprisonment about the little farm was replaced by a feeling of release, almost of spring.

This in turn led to a certain atmosphere of carelessness. For the last few snow-gripped days she went about on guard, fearful of a crow-shadow or the noise of a plane, constantly listening for the voice of the sergeant, a knock on the door. During all this time she made Barton stay indoors. Sometimes, for half a day, while she fed and milked the cow, fed the hens and collected eggs, he lay in bed, reading or dozing or listening to music on a small portable radio. She had no cause to resent this. The fact of his being safely out of sight increased, on the contrary, her sense of security, and at last of carelessness.

On a fine soft afternoon, some days before Christmas, she cycled down to the shop to buy her weekly groceries. Like a child with an unexpected toy, she was thrilled almost to dancing by the discovery of a tin of pilchards and a pot of gold paint. Her thoughts were on a Christmas party. Three years of Christmas at war had already blessed women, at Christmas time, with a capacity for much ingenuity. She would paint branches of yew and holly with gold. There were no limits as to what you could do with things: acorns and pine-cones, branches

of rose-hips, heads of teazle seed, beech branches, skeletons of leaves. She had even met a neighbour who had wrought patterns of much beauty out of gilded fish-bones.

As she rode home, stopping on the way through the wood to break off an occasional bough of holly or acorns or yew or beech still thick with husks, her sense of carelessness became complete. She hadn't seen the tanks for days. The entire valley lay below her like a huge green pond, virgin, smoothly peaceful.

THE TRIPLE ECHO

EVERY YEAR the elderly Miss Rigby and the slightly older Miss Pinkerton, affectionately known to each other as Spud and Pinkie, celebrated some part of Christmas by having a few glasses of port, a slice of plum cake and a wedge of Cheshire cheese in the old air-raid shelter that still stood, after so many years, under their bottom garden wall.

'Sort of thanksgiving for what we got through at the time,' they would explain.

Late in the autumn, after the leaves of the pumpkins that always grew on the roof of the shelter had been blackened to sloppy pulp by the first frosts, Pinkie raked off the old dead vines, scrubbed down the interior corrugated iron with strong carbolic soap and opened the door for several days to give the shelter what she called 'a bit of a sweetener'.

Pinkie was small, very cherubic and fierily red in the face, with light blue eyes that protruded eagerly like little silver thimbles. After a few drops of what she called 'the you know what' she glowed hotly, with positively mustard-like excitement, and chattered with panting merriment, looking like a breathless Pekinese. In the household she rushed from object to object in sniffing and palpitating pursuit, as if everywhere seeking a hidden bone.

Miss Rigby, Spud, was neither so active nor so lucky. She was big, slow, imperturbable and misshapen. Her face was so like a large discoloured potato that the name Spud really suited her. She suffered, among other things, from painful swellings of the legs, uneasy shortness of breath and false teeth that didn't fit very well and continually got gummed together by pieces of marshmallow, her favourite sweetmeat. But these minor pains never discouraged her. She waddled everywhere with wheezy and jovial optimism, sometimes carrying large orange pumpkins about, nursing them in her arms like fat babies to which she had miraculously given birth

In the shelter all the antique paraphernalia of war-time – the war was so far away and yet sometimes seemed like only yesterday – was preserved as it had always been: stirrup pump and two buckets, one of water and one of sand, torch, candle in its holder, whistle and even a pair of gas-masks neatly hung in their khaki bags on the wall.

A small square window, its glass of the kind that is reinforced with wire, gave out on to the garden, and here Spud and Pinkie sat on the afternoon of Christmas Eve, gazing at the damp earth outside, sipping port-wine and munching on cake and cheese.

'We always seem to have good weather,' Pinkie said. 'Goodness knows what we'd do if it snowed.'

'Of course you know what we'd do if it snowed,' Spud said. 'We'd sit here just the same. It would take more than that to put us off.'

'I suppose so. I suppose so. I suppose it would, Spud dear.'

'Do you remember how it snowed in 1940?' Spud said. 'We got snowed in and there were enormous drifts and we couldn't get out again.'

They laughed in chorus at this: Spud rather like a deep French horn, Pinkie like a cymbal.

'And I blew so hard on the whistle to get Mr Ackerly to come and dig us out I thought I'd blow my teeth out,' Spud said. 'I always say that's what first loosened them.'

They laughed again at this and Pinkie poured more port. It didn't seem like Christmas until they were well on with the port and they could hear the evening bells across the town. The candle always made a difference too and presently Spud said:

'Let's have the candle alight, shall we, Pinkie? I love the glow of the port in the candlelight.'

'I'll do it, Spud dear, I'll do it. Don't move.'

In the candlelight it was not only the port that glowed. Pinkie glowed too, a fiery little cherub flashing silver thimble-eyes.

'Funny how the candle all of a sudden makes it seem dark outside,' she said. 'And then you see that wonderful blue in the sky. And the first stars.'

'They say the band will be coming this way on Christmas Eve this year,' Spud said, 'instead of Christmas morning.'

'Oh! do they? I didn't put their Christmas-box ready. You think I ought to pop back and get it in case they arrive?'

'No, no. Sit still. We shall hear them when they come.'

'You mean we will if we don't drop off. You remember the year we both dropped off? And slept through that awful raid? Sound as babies. And everybody said how ghastly it was.'

They laughed again at this stirring and hilarious memory and Pinkie poured out a further drop of port. War was awfully funny, really, depending on how you looked at it.

'I don't see it starting to rain, do I?' Pinkie huffed on the little glass window and then rubbed it with the sleeve of her musquash coat and peered out. 'No, I don't think so.' She champed on a piece of plum cake like an eager puppy. 'I tell you what I do see, though. There's somebody in the garden. Wandering around.'

'Not the Angel Gabriel, is it?' Spud said. 'We don't want him here. Not yet, anyway.'

This was the signal for another jovial duet of laughter and then Pinkie opened the door of the shelter and called:

'Hullo there. Who is it? Who's about?'

An answering voice called 'Hullo there!' and Pinkie said:

'Oh! it's you, Mr Ackerly. We're in here. In the shelter.'

'What's come over him?' Spud said. 'He doesn't usually call till Christmas Day. Everybody's changing their habits.'

'Come in, Mr Ackerly, if you can get in,' Pinkie said. 'Come and join us.'

'Yes,' Spud said, 'come and join our happy throng.'

Mr Ackerly, a tall stooping figure looking rather like a pessimistic giraffe with a bowler hat on, appeared from the outer gloom, carrying a bottle wrapped in tissue paper.

'What a nice surprise,' Spud said. 'What brings you on Christmas Eve? You usually come tomorrow.'

'Oh! I don't know.' Pessimism oozed out of Mr Ackerly like dark vapour; there was almost a cloud about the candle. 'After all, there might not *be* a tomorrow.'

'Now don't start talking about The Bomb again,' Spud said. 'It's Christmas Eve.'

'No, no, not The Bomb, please,' Pinkie said. 'Have a drop of port. I'll go and get another glass for you.'

'Oh! I don't know if I should –'

'Oh! of course you should!' Spud said. 'Sit down. I don't like you standing up. You're so tall I feel you'll lift our dear old shelter off its feet.'

While Pinkie raced puppy-like across the garden to get another glass from the house, Mr Ackerly sat down and stared about him with increasing gloom. Our dear old shelter – did you ever hear anything like it? Heavens, it was awful. Whatever made them do it every year? Dear old shelter – there was a terrible monkish sort of odour about the place that repelled him. The mould of death lay on it – it really made him shudder.

Candlelight always depressed him too, anyway. What with that and The Bomb it seemed a pretty desolate outlook, he thought, as he sat there staring at Spud, the trembling candle and all the silly, derelict paraphernalia of wartime. He couldn't for the life of him fathom what made them do it. The future was bleak enough without dragging up the past.

Cheerfully, actually humming a few bars of *Christians Awake!*, Pinkie came back from the house with a glass for Mr Ackerly.

'Just a modicum,' Mr Ackerly said. 'That's ample –'

The sight of Pinkie pouring the port reminded Mr Ackerly that he was the bearer of a gift. With a struggling sigh he handed over the bottle to Spud as if it were The Bomb itself.

'Just my usual little offering to both of you.' He seemed to be about to render the first notes of a sepulchral anthem.

'You'd better drink it up quick. If you ask me we haven't got much time.'

Pinkie shut the door of the shelter and Spud ripped off the tissue wrapping of the bottle as if it concealed a new hat.

'Oh! our favourite whisky. Nice man. Thank you so awfully much,' Spud said. 'Kiss.'

Mr Ackerly, with despondent reluctance, suffered himself to be kissed first on one cheek by Spud and then on the other by Pinkie.

'How nice. How generous of you. Well, cheers,' Spud said. 'Here's to Christmas. And the best of luck in the future.'

'Great Heavens, we'll need it,' Mr Ackerly said. 'No, we won't

138

though, because there isn't going to be any.'

'Any what?' Spud said. 'Future? Don't talk out of your back collar-stud, man.'

'Everybody was saying that in 1940,' Pinkie said. 'And dear knows they were the dark days –'

'Ah!' Mr Ackerly said, 'but this is different. This is different.'

Spud laughed again, French-horn fashion, and held out her glass.

'I'll have a drop more, Pinkie dear, please. I need fortifying.'

'We all do,' Mr Ackerly said.

'That's why I say "Drink up your bottle while you can." There isn't much time. There can't be.'

'I vote we do that,' Spud said. 'What say, Pinkie? I feel in that mood.'

'You know me,' Pinkie said. 'I'm game for anything. Especially the you know what. It's Christmas anyway.'

THE OLD ETERNAL

THE MORNING broke grey and bitter: not the day he had hoped for. A brutish wind went driving through the oak-woods, rattling at dead leaves. Out across exposed fields it whined over naked hedgerows, cutting like glass at the balls of his eyes. It was a day without light, and by afternoon the chill was clenched and sullen in his bones.

THE SLEEPLESS MOON

THE RITUAL of street games went on freely and unhampered, summer and winter, except in the very severest weather. There was no danger. A bicycle or two, a baker's cart trundling home with its golden candles trembling in the lamps, a late horse-drawn dray delivering a load of belly leather or packing cases to a factory before going back to the railway yards: these were about the only hazards we might expect to disturb us. The street was not only ours; we were expected, and ordered, to play there.

So, fortified in my case by hot tea, hot toast spread with home-made lard and salt – and how very good it was – we all went out, on early winter evenings, to the gas-lit street stage. I remember the winter evenings more vividly, I suppose, than the summer ones simply because of the gas-light: the one big street light round which we played

Sally go Round the Moon
Sally go Round the Stars
Sally go Round the Chimney Pot
On a Sunday afternoon

and the lights of the three shops.

Almost always, I think, we first gathered round the window of one of the baker's shops to sort out preliminaries for play. Certain preliminaries had always to be gone through, among them the picking of teams, and also 'who was going to start it'. We always did this by rhymes. Thus, as we gathered in a circle, one of us went round, pointing to each in turn, reciting:

Paddy on the railway, picking up stones,
Down came the engine and broke Paddy's bones.
Well, said Paddy, that isn't fair.
Well, said the engine, I don't care.
O – U – T spells
'Out Goes She'

or we varied it thus:

> *Ink, Pink*
> *I think*
> *There is*
> *A stink*
> *And it comes from*
> *Y O U !*
> *O – U – T spells*
> *'Out Goes She'*

After this the teams divided up, one going to the far side of the street, the other remaining by the shop window, so to speak on home ground. The main games in this category, in all probability having origins going back for centuries, were *I Apprentice My Son, I Spy, Three Old Men Come Workhouse* and *What's Your Trade?* though the last two may well have been slightly different versions of the same thing.

THE VANISHED WORLD

A DAY later, to her intense relief, snow began to fall again. She watched it from the windows of the house as a child would watch it, bewitched by transformation. Slowly at first, then in big soggy flakes and then under the driven power of a north-easter that skimmed it up into swift white vapours that piled eventually into drifts shaped against the hillside like curving scimitars, brooding white beasts or measureless glistening caverns of salt, the snow created its fast barricade of imprisonment.

When it stopped at last and she went for the first time to open the kitchen door a great avalanche fell in on her, a breaking drift the height of a man.

She was overjoyed. The sense of imprisonment created by the vastness of snow brought back a feeling of inviolate security. Again she felt herself and Barton to be cut off from the world: the world of the sergeant, the tanks, the dance, the ludicrous jest of Christmas Eve. This white imprisonment also uplifted her. Paradoxically, wonderfully, she felt free.

There were now three days to go before Christmas.

'It's going to be a white one,' she said. 'It can snow for a week. I've got everything. We won't starve. I've even got two red candles. At the shop they said they've saved a few from before the war.'

When the snow at last stopped she felt totally embalmed in its world of pure white silence. The immediate past lost itself somewhere beyond the boundaries of a great tranquillity. Without ever saying it, she regretted deeply all she had said in anger. Her tenderness for him returned.

'We said a lot of things we didn't mean,' was her way of expressing all she felt. 'We never meant all those things.'

You could, she said to him once, fairly listen to the snow silence. And had he noticed, now that the sun had come out again, how the shadows were blue?

In the white, blue-shadowed world she saw, in broad daylight, a big dog fox ambling with a sort of careless stealth across a piece of ploughed land from which strong wind had so swept the surface snow that it was now a corrugation of black and white.

'I'll have that one,' she said.

She got the gun and in gum–boots tramped out into the snow. She actually caught a second glimpse of the fox as she climbed the gate leading out of the farmyard. Then he suddenly paused, lifted his head, seemed to sniff at the air, then as suddenly doubled back on his tracks, slipped into a hedge of blackthorn and disappeared.

THE TRIPLE ECHO

ADAM WAS aroused one morning in January by the gaunt figure of his grandmother standing over the bed with a candle in her hand. He became aware in a dreamy way of her bony hand shaking his shoulder, her old, cracked voice telling him smartly: 'Slip into your things; it's half-past six,' and then of the cold vacant room and the candle which she had left burning before the white face of the clock standing by the bedside. Getting up, pulling on his cold trousers over his warm, sleepy legs, and feeling the ice-cold air take its vicious sweeps at him through the cracks at the window, he felt half-blind with sleep and oppressed by wretchedness, as though being driven to something against his will. He was conscious of hating the naked ticking of the clock and the cold white stick of candle burning unsteadily. And all this seemed only to emphasize the silent, freezing winter morning darkness, which he hated above all.

CHARLOTTE'S ROW

DURING THE remaining days of December and on into the early days of January he went to the house as she had suggested, two or three evenings a week, or even more if the weather were bad, and she gave him lessons in handwriting and simple arithmetic. He would sit on one side of the table and she on the other, a pale rose tasselled shawl spread over the mahogany and a sheet of newspaper over the shawl to catch the ink-drops. They would begin with a glass of wine and end with one. It was so warm and comfortable there, with the fire and the wine, that a curious sense of pleasant lethargy would come over him, a feeling that nothing mattered. She set him exercises to copy, exercises of unexacting simplicity which only heightened that sense of unambitious lethargy. And seeing him sometimes grow bored with the slow copying or multiplication she would suggest that he read instead. 'We'll both read,' she would say. 'What book shall it be, eh?' And he would say, 'Don't matter to me.' Then she would pick up the lamp and take it to the bookshelves and make a pretence of searching among the titles. 'Supposing we read Fox's *Martyrs*?' The book was always the same and as she read from it, slowly and smoothly, knowing the words off by heart, he would fall half-asleep in that dim atmosphere of wine and soft words and mellow lamplight.

THE POACHER

145

THE LAST days of January tore themselves out in a wild gale. For three days the wind drove across the land in a moaning frenzy and rain lashed against the farmhouse and the barns and hissed and roared in the spinney like a stormy sea, flooding the yards and filling the dykes. The shriek of wind and rain, the murmur of rushing waters, the whipping and cracking of trees in the spinney made a chorus of wild and mournful sound. The ploughed land was beaten into a dead morass, the furrows turning to dykes of muddy water. The fallow field was flooded at its shallow end.

THE FALLOW LAND

EVER SINCE daybreak a strong east wind had raged, the trees had kept up a savage moaning and the clouds had shrunk into a drab, solid mass. And all day the sun had not shone, and only at evening, when sinking, had glowed for one instant on the tree-tops, the black roofs of the barns, the steeple of the church and the sombre sky.

As Israel Rentshaw came home through his paddock, hobbling badly, he stopped to bring in his horse, a lean old thing which hobbled too, and struggling slowly against this wind, which now and then tore out the ends of his red neckerchief and whipped across his face strands of his horse's mane, led the nag through the orchard towards the white farmhouse visible at the far end. In the dusky orchard the apple-trees, the cherry-trees and the damsons all looked black and alike. About Israel and the horse kept flying pieces of straw, feathers of ducks and hens, and twigs which snapped off the trees and fell in a pattering shower. Close at hand a pond fringed with alders and poplars gleamed, and beyond were visible groups of black wooden barns, stacks of straw and hay, manure-heaps, old carts, harrows, heaps of stone and drainage pipes covered with dead weeds. Further off dim shapes of woods slept and solitary trees and endless stretches of fields. But a mile away the river by which the village rested, the meadows and the village itself were already lost in darkness.

DAY'S END

ONE WINTER afternoon, in the yard, he stood idle under the cart-hovel, watching a hare. Rain had been falling heavily all day. He could see the dark reflected clouds in the vast acres of flood-water extending far along the valley. The hare, light-coloured, almost golden against the rain-soaked earth, was running diagonally across the field in sudden starts of play and alarm, doubling and loping from side to side as it made for the lower hedge. He waited for it to disappear. Rain was still falling, in desultory spits that flecked and ringed the clay-coloured puddles about the yard. The hare was full-grown, a beauty. Then it struck him suddenly that it was the first he had noticed in the field. If he had ever seen another it had been unconsciously. And he stood transfixed in wonder.

When the hare had disappeared he found a length of wire and walked down the field, looping the wire as he went. The spot where the hare had vanished was clear in his mind. The land was sodden, the water squelching back everywhere into his footmarks. It was late January, his winter wheat was up and the young corn shoots lay flattened on the earth, like wet flags. As he went along under the hedge his shoulders brushed off drops of rain that hung on the reddish hawthorn twigs like beads of ice. And standing still he could see where the hare had capered across the wheat. Its little footprints had filled up, like his own, with yellowish water. And then he saw the gap. He went down on his knees to examine it. He could see by the broken brown skin of the split hawthorn twigs and the foot-padded earth that it was quite old. It had been in use a long time. Mystified, he thought: 'I ain't above half-alive. Damn, I must go about with me eyes shut.' He had scarcely to press back a twig or move a single grass in order to set his snare. It seemed too good to be true. And as he threaded the wire-loop and sharpened the ash-peg he felt a strange sense of excitement. He could hardly bear it. Something out of his past life came back to him, like a suddenly recollected emotion. His hands made the wire-loop almost unconsciously. He was like a swimmer cutting the water for the first time after a long absence. He sharpened the ash-peg carefully, and then slit it, very lightly, and then turned it round and round in his hands and looked at it. It was a beautiful peg. He had never made a better peg. Then he went down on his knees and looked at the gap again. He squinted through it like a man taking a gun-sight. Beyond the hedge the next field was pasture. By squinting through the run he could see across the grass the thin slightly padded tracks the hares had made by running to and fro. There were two tracks; and then he saw a third. They converged upon the gap like wheel-spokes. That meant that there were three at least and perhaps more hares passing regularly from one field to another. He stood up. He could scarcely believe it. He had been going about with his eyes shut. He had been so absorbed in the breaking up and planting of the field that he couldn't see what was under his own eyes. Christ, he was a born fool! He wiped the wire with his handkerchief and then, instinctively, without thinking, glanced round the field. There was not a soul in sight; nothing moving except the desultory rain and the boughs of the distant ash trees swinging flexibly up and down in the wind. He bent down and with his handkerchief gloved over his fingers set the snare. He moved with extreme lightness, scarcely touching the wire. And then, having finished it, he stepped back, at first two paces and then another. At the third pace the peg and the wire could no longer be distinguished from the twigs of hawthorn.

In the morning, coming down the field in the half-daylight, he found the hare, a buck, dead in the gap. There was no sign of a struggle, no blood, no torn fur. The wire had pulled up with extraordinary smoothness, like lightning, throttling the hare in a second. He felt a sense of almost fierce elation as he unwound the snare and put the wire in his pocket and went up the field with the hare in his hand.

THE POACHER

149

ACROSS THE ice, all that afternoon, the sunlight was a wintry apricot, deep and fiery above the edges of flat horizons smoky-blue with frost. Skates sang shrill and then deep and thrilling across empty meadows in the lovely air. There were a lot of people there that I knew that day and whenever I passed them they stared at me, not speaking, because of the strange new girl I had with me.

She moved through all the early afternoon like a girl whose limbs have never been used. Her hands were quite fierce and terrified as they clutched at me. She held her head too high, too stiff and too far backwards, and her body went forward as if on stilts. All her in-breeding, her seclusion and what I took to be a genteel physical frustration came out that afternoon in a painful wooden awkwardness that made her more clumsy than ever. We fell down every ten yards or so. Everywhere people were falling down in the same way, shrieking and laughing, but she did not laugh when she fell down. She got to her feet every time with a look of remarkable intensity, with dark eyes fixed ahead.

LOVE FOR LYDIA

But the picture of that winter night of the party at the farmhouse needs little cleaning. The varnish of time has certainly obscured many of the faces that were there, but I still see clearly the big farm kitchen, the huge low-ceilinged sitting-room, the girls in their typical nineteen-twenty dresses and the piles of home-made cakes, tarts, sandwiches, jellies, cheeses and sausage rolls. I can still smell the soft milkiness of the kitchen, the whiff of frigid cow-pungent winter air as the back door was opened and the wood-smoke of the farmhouse fires. As the evening went on we ate, drank – not a single thimble of alcohol of any kind, naturally – danced, played games, gossiped and flirted.

We danced, I suppose, to a gramophone. The games were simple: mostly, I think, charades. But from time to time there was much running up and down the bare ancient oak stairs, phases of hide-and-seek and the usual hilarity, accompanied by shrieking, as if seductions of some sort were taking place in the upper darkness. For my own part I remember getting tired of dancing, exchanging shallow gossip and generally running around. At last, I suppose somewhere towards midnight, I found myself sitting on the half-dark stairs with a girl I had never met before: fair-haired, blue-eyed, rather petite and barely seventeen.

I have always fancied myself to be rather quickwitted but she, it turned out, was just as quick. Though she was in fact a stranger to me I got the impression that I had in fact met her before. The truth is that I somehow mixed her up with someone else. This led to a certain confusion, further leading to light banter, in the conversation.

I asked her name.

'Marjorie,' she told me. 'But most people call me Madge.'

I told her my name.

'I know,' she said.

Soon after this, since it was only a day or two beyond Valentine's Day, I teasingly hinted that she must have received a heap of Valentines. By so doing I opened up a mystery. There was a certain special Valentine she could not account for. She didn't suppose that I could? With a growing sense of mischief I hinted that it wasn't beyond the bounds of possibility. With excitement and curiosity she begged to know who had sent it, while I, with the sense of mischief growing all the time, succeeded merely in making the mystery grow darker and darker, more and more excited. Without my ever having uttered a word to confirm it, it was clear before midnight that I was the Valentine's sender. I had in fact never sent a Valentine to a girl in my life but that night it was an unsent Valentine – unsent by me, that is – that introduced me to the affections of the girl I was eventually to marry.

THE VANISHED WORLD

AFTER THE death of their elder brother the two Aspen sisters came back to Evensford at the end of February, driving in the enormous brown coachwork Daimler with the gilt monograms on the doors, through a sudden fall of snow.

Across the valley the floods of January, frozen to wide lakes of ice, were cut into enormous rectangular patterns by black hedgerows that lay like a wreckage of logs washed down on the broken river. A hard dark wind blew straight across the ice from the north-east, beating in at that end of the town where for a few hundred yards the High Street runs straight, past what is now Johnson's car-wrecking yard, under the railway arches, and then between the high causeways that make it like a dry canal. It was so cold that solid ice seemed to be whipped up from the valley on the wind, to explode into whirlwinds of harsh and bitter dust that pranced about in stinging clouds. Ice formed everywhere in dry black pools, polished in sheltered places, ruckled with dark waves at street corners or on sloping gutters where wind had flurried the last falls of rain.

LOVE FOR LYDIA

ALL DAY the February earth had lain under an immense lid of cloud. The woods, full of green saplings and shaggy older trees, laboured futilely against a fast-driven rain which soaked them steadily. Down the trunks rivulets of water rushed continuously, ending in dark pools at the feet of the trees. From the summit of the hill where the cottage stood, sodden and dark but for a square of light under its north eave, the road wound like a shallow yellow stream.

THE SHEPHERD

THE MAN cutting the hedge between the roadside and the field of winter wheat was quite young and slight. But he was wearing gloves: large hedger's gloves, having deep gauntlets scarred and ripped by thorns of bramble and haw, and for some reason they gave him an appearance of greater age and muscularity. The hedge, old and wild, branched high up with great trunks of ash and hawthorn dwarfed and thickened and misshapen by long confinement with each other. And the young man was laying it: half-splitting the boughs at the foot and bending them prostrate and staking them into a new order. He worked slowly, but with concentration, rather fiercely, and almost at times with anger. In the mild February air the sweat broke out on his fair skin abundantly, renewing itself as soon as he had wiped it away. He would take off his right glove repeatedly in order to wipe his face with his hand; and once he dropped it and it lay on the ground like a flat dry pancake of cow-dung. He picked it up, swore, and flapped it across his knee with exclamations of anger that were really against himself.

CUT AND COME AGAIN

THE ORCHARDS begin to move into life as far back as February, sometimes in January, in warm winters in December: not cherries or plums or apples, but orchards of hazel, which hang out avenues of slanting, honey-green catkins that seem smokily luminous in the flat winter sun.

In the whole English fruit year there is nothing quite like this first soft wintry blossoming of millions of catkins, when countless flowers swing away from the wind together and stand out horizontally in air, poised in golden parallel, almost flying, then falling away and dancing in the moments of dead calm.

The avenues are so straight and formal and the pruning of the trees so rigid that the catkins seem like irresponsible things, too frisky and delicate for squat trees pruned of their grace. And I imagine hardly anyone ever sees these first nut orchards blooming in mid-winter; and I imagine, too, that for every hundred persons who see them only one, perhaps, sees their millions of other flowers: the almost invisible firmament of minute female flowers, like ragged scarlet stars, that hide behind the dancing curtains of the males.

IN THE HEART OF THE COUNTRY

SOURCES AND ACKNOWLEDGEMENTS

The extracts in this book have been chosen from the copyright volumes listed below. The publishers are grateful to the various publishers involved, and to the copyright owners, for their courteous permission to make this selection from the entire range of H.E. Bates's novels, short stories, memoirs and essays.

'Day's End', 'The Shepherd', 'The Fuel–Gatherers', 'Fishing' from *Day's End* Jonathan Cape 1928

Catherine Foster Jonathan Cape 1929, Severn House 1988

Charlotte's Row Jonathan Cape 1931

The Fallow Land Jonathan Cape 1932, Robinson Publishing 1988

'On the Road', 'A Flower Piece', 'The Mower' from *The Black Boxer* Jonathan Cape 1932, from *Seven by Five* Michael Joseph 1963

'Innocence', 'The Lily' from *The Woman Who Had Imagination* Jonathan Cape 1934

'Cut and Come Again', 'The Plough' from *Cut and Come Again* Jonathan Cape 1935

The Poacher Jonathan Cape 1935, Robinson Publishing 1984

Through the Woods Victor Gollancz 1936

A House of Women Jonathan Cape 1936, Severn House 1988

'Breeze Anstey' from *Something Short and Sweet* Jonathan Cape 1937, from *Seven by Five* Michael Joseph 1963

Spella Ho Jonathan Cape 1938, Severn House 1989

In the Heart of the Country Country Life 1942, Robinson Publishing 1985

'The Little Farm', 'The Lighthouse' from *Colonel Julian* Michael Joseph 1951

The Country of White Clover Michael Joseph 1952, Alan Sutton 1984

Love for Lydia Michael Joseph 1952

'Dulcima', 'The Grass God' from *The Nature of Love* Michael Joseph 1953

The Feast of July Michael Joseph 1954

'The Good Corn', 'Chaff in the Wind' from *The Daffodil Sky* Michael Joseph 1955

The Sleepless Moon Michael Joseph 1956

'The Death of a Huntsman', 'Night Run to the West', 'The Queen of Spain Fritillary' from *The Death of a Huntsman* Michael Joseph 1957

The Darling Buds of May Michael Joseph 1958

'The Watercress Girl', 'Great Uncle Crow' from *The Watercress Girl* Michael Joseph 1959

When the Green Woods Laugh Michael Joseph 1960

Oh! To Be in England Michael Joseph 1963

A Moment in Time Michael Joseph 1964

'Shandy Lil', 'The Sun of December', 'The Old Eternal' from *The Wedding Party* Michael Joseph 1965

'The Simple Life', 'The Four Beauties' from *The Four Beauties* Michael Joseph 1968

The Vanished World Michael Joseph 1969, Robinson Publishing 1987

A Little of What You Fancy Michael Joseph 1970

The Triple Echo Michael Joseph 1970

The Blossoming World Michael Joseph 1971

The World in Ripeness Michael Joseph 1972, from *The Ripening World* Robinson Publishing 1988

'The Man Who Loved Squirrels' from *The Song of the Wren* Michael Joseph 1972

The Yellow Meads of Asphodel Michael Joseph 1976